Two Grade 1 Arithmetic

by
K. Lovell B.Sc., M.A., Ph.D. (Lond.)

Professor of Educational Psychology,
University of Leeds

and
C.H.J. Smith B.Sc., M.A., Ph.D. (Lond.)

formerly Senior Lecturer in Education and
Methodology of Mathematics,
Borough Road College

Ginn and Company Ltd

Revised and reset 1969
First metric edition 1971
Revised metric edition 1975
Revised edition 1981
Sixteenth impression 1996 019610

ISBN 0 602 22536 1 (without answers)
ISBN 0 602 22537 X (with answers)

Published by Ginn and Company
Prebendal House, Parson's Fee, Aylesbury, Bucks HP20 2QY

Printed in Great Britain by Athenæum Press Ltd, Gateshead, Tyne & Wear

PREFACE

I hope that these books will give you experience of working some important kinds of examples. Those on the right hand page are usually a little harder than those on the left.

Your teacher will tell you which examples you should work. If you try hard and work steadily and neatly, I hope you will get right all the exercises that you attempt, and that you come to enjoy mathematics.

Leeds
1980

K. LOVELL

ADDITION

All can try these

1   2
   +1
	2 3
	   +6
		3 7
		   +4
			4 5
			   +1
				5 7
				   +0

6   1
   +8
	7 2
	   +5
		8 3
		   +7
			9 2
			   +4
				10 8
				   +1

11   4
   +0
	12 9
	   +9
		13 6
		   +5
			14 8
			   +7
				15 1
				   +1

16   4
   +6
	17 1
	   +2
		18 6
		   +0
			19 7
			   +6
				20 5
				   +3

21   0
   +9
	22 8
	   +5
		23 6
		   +9
			24 0
			   +1
				25 4
				   +4

26   2
   +6
	27 9
	   +5
		28 1
		   +0
			29 7
			   +9
				30 2
				   +8

31 $0+0$ **32** $6+4$ **33** $8+3$ **34** $5+7$

35 $6+3$ **36** $7+5$ **37** $6+8$ **38** $0+3$

39 $5+8$ **40** $3+1$ **41** $7+7$ **42** $9+0$

43 $4+2$ **44** $0+4$ **45** $6+1$ **46** $2+2$

47 $7+3$ **48** $5+2$ **49** $1+9$ **50** $7+8$

ADDITION

All can try these

1 1 +3	**2** 7 +2	**3** 9 +1	**4** 8 +0	**5** 2 +3
6 5 +6	**7** 1 +4	**8** 9 +8	**9** 2 +0	**10** 4 +9
11 6 +7	**12** 0 +6	**13** 3 +2	**14** 1 +6	**15** 8 +9
16 0 +5	**17** 9 +7	**18** 4 +3	**19** 0 +8	**20** 9 +3
21 5 +9	**22** 8 +2	**23** 5 +0	**24** 3 +3	**25** 4 +1
26 6 +6	**27** 0 +7	**28** 2 +9	**29** 8 +6	**30** 4 +5

31 0 + 2   **32** 3 + 4   **33** 4 + 8   **34** 5 + 5

35 8 + 4   **36** 3 + 5   **37** 8 + 8   **38** 9 + 2

39 3 + 9   **40** 4 + 7   **41** 5 + 4   **42** 3 + 8

43 9 + 6   **44** 3 + 0   **45** 6 + 2   **46** 1 + 7

47 9 + 4   **48** 1 + 5   **49** 2 + 7   **50** 7 + 1

SUBTRACTION

All can try these

1 7 − 5	**2** 2 − 2	**3** 4 − 1	**4** 9 − 0	**5** 5 − 3

6 8 − 6	**7** 5 − 0	**8** 7 − 3	**9** 6 − 2	**10** 4 − 4

11 6 − 0	**12** 9 − 8	**13** 4 − 3	**14** 1 − 1	**15** 7 − 2

16 0 − 0	**17** 3 − 2	**18** 7 − 4	**19** 1 − 0	**20** 7 − 1

21 9 − 2	**22** 5 − 1	**23** 6 − 5	**24** 8 − 7	**25** 4 − 0

26 7 − 6	**27** 4 − 2	**28** 9 − 3	**29** 2 − 1	**30** 8 − 2

31 2 − 0   **32** 9 − 9   **33** 8 − 5   **34** 3 − 1

35 6 − 6   **36** 5 − 4   **37** 6 − 3   **38** 9 − 1

39 8 − 8   **40** 7 − 0   **41** 8 − 4   **42** 3 − 0

43 6 − 4   **44** 5 − 5   **45** 8 − 1   **46** 9 − 6

47 3 − 3   **48** 5 − 2   **49** 9 − 5   **50** 8 − 0

SUBTRACTION

All can try these

1	8 −3	**2**	6 −1	**3**	9 −4	**4**	7 −7	**5**	10 −2
6	9 −7	**7**	12 −9	**8**	13 −6	**9**	10 −7	**10**	11 −2
11	14 −7	**12**	12 −6	**13**	10 −4	**14**	11 −5	**15**	10 −6
16	11 −8	**17**	10 −1	**18**	16 −8	**19**	12 −4	**20**	10 −8
21	11 −7	**22**	14 −8	**23**	10 −3	**24**	15 −7	**25**	11 −4
26	10 −9	**27**	15 −9	**28**	14 −5	**29**	12 −7	**30**	14 −6

31 11 − 3   **32** 12 − 5   **33** 16 − 7   **34** 17 − 9

35 15 − 8   **36** 13 − 4   **37** 11 − 9   **38** 13 − 7

39 12 − 3   **40** 18 − 9   **41** 17 − 8   **42** 13 − 9

43 11 − 6   **44** 13 − 5   **45** 10 − 5   **46** 14 − 9

47 12 − 8   **48** 16 − 9   **49** 13 − 8   **50** 15 − 6

ADDITION

First try these

1	10 +2	**2**	15 +1	**3**	12 +4	**4**	11 +3
5	5 +13	**6**	18 +3	**7**	6 +15	**8**	19 +4
9	16 +7	**10**	5 +17	**11**	13 +11	**12**	12 +14
13	15 +10	**14**	16 +11	**15**	12 +12	**16**	29 +3
17	36 +5	**18**	28 +4	**19**	24 +6	**20**	35 +5
21	25 +13	**22**	16 +31	**23**	20 +19	**24**	37 +12
25	44 +15	**26**	14 +28	**27**	26 +26	**28**	27 +23
29	25 +36	**30**	41 +19	**31**	54 +62	**32**	30 +80
33	94 +21	**34**	85 +42	**35**	72 +73	**36**	61 +28

ADDITION

Now try these

1   13
    +4

2   15
    +3

3   6
   +11

4   10
    +9

5   12
    +7

6   14
    +8

7   5
   +18

8   19
    +6

9   17
    +9

10   6
   +16

11   12
   +17

12   10
   +18

13   15
   +14

14   14
   +12

15   13
   +13

16   24
    +7

17   39
    +5

18   41
    +9

19   37
    +4

20   64
    +8

21   36
   +63

22   74
   +20

23   58
   +31

24   50
   +27

25   45
   +42

26   29
   +56

27   39
   +41

28   18
   +47

29   65
   +26

30   38
   +23

31   65
   +51

32   80
   +63

33   27
   +90

34   74
   +95

35   83
   +46

36   97
   +85

SUBTRACTION

First try these

1	37 – 4	**2**	28 – 3	**3**	19 – 6	**4**	48 – 8
5	26 – 5	**6**	25 – 2	**7**	39 – 1	**8**	59 – 9
9	44 – 3	**10**	38 – 6	**11**	26 – 14	**12**	48 – 26
13	49 – 37	**14**	55 – 22	**15**	29 – 16	**16**	43 – 23
17	57 – 12	**18**	64 – 41	**19**	36 – 21	**20**	70 – 40
21	19 – 11	**22**	24 – 22	**23**	39 – 35	**24**	46 – 43
25	37 – 30	**26**	34 – 7	**27**	21 – 5	**28**	42 – 9
29	56 – 8	**30**	33 – 4	**31**	32 – 16	**32**	51 – 29
33	25 – 19	**34**	52 – 28	**35**	41 – 26	**36**	31 – 18

SUBTRACTION

Now try these

1	78 – 6	**2**	94 – 3	**3**	59 – 7	**4**	65 – 5
5	87 – 4	**6**	99 – 9	**7**	54 – 1	**8**	49 – 8
9	75 – 3	**10**	85 – 5	**11**	83 – 21	**12**	90 – 40
13	76 – 52	**14**	49 – 31	**15**	68 – 46	**16**	96 – 25
17	37 – 16	**18**	55 – 20	**19**	84 – 62	**20**	78 – 48
21	49 – 43	**22**	98 – 91	**23**	17 – 12	**24**	54 – 50
25	87 – 86	**26**	63 – 8	**27**	54 – 7	**28**	81 – 3
29	75 – 6	**30**	88 – 9	**31**	58 – 39	**32**	95 – 78
33	82 – 17	**34**	64 – 59	**35**	73 – 36	**36**	21 – 14

ADDITION

First try these

Set 1

1	38 +73	**2**	57 +65	**3**	82 +59	**4**	67 +53

5	54 29 +36	**6**	13 98 +20	**7**	5 67 +51	**8**	49 17 +83

9	32 +127	**10**	421 +151	**11**	506 +243	**12**	417 +401

13	127 +346	**14**	419 +253	**15**	372 +195	**16**	280 +669

17	256 +178	**18**	439 +386	**19**	563 +99	**20**	275 +648

Set 2

1 21 + 18 + 2

2 30 + 14 + 5

3 17 + 11 + 22

4 40 + 3 + 12

5 19 + 54 + 6

6 7 + 42 + 15

7 56 + 13 + 10

8 28 + 61 + 8

9 69 + 38 + 14

10 83 + 17 + 50

11 32 + 97 + 205

12 164 + 12 + 100

13 263 + 40 + 58

14 81 + 27 + 188 + 33

15 90 + 217 + 56 + 68

16 48 + 197 + 301 + 10

ADDITION

Now try these

1	57 +68	**2**	94 +56	**3**	83 +59	**4**	67 +76
5	73 45 +8	**6**	80 46 +29	**7**	93 28 +81	**8**	78 3 +95
9	147 +232	**10**	43 +621	**11**	805 +43	**12**	812 +275
13	268 +105	**14**	234 +574	**15**	453 +281	**16**	490 +629
17	784 +196	**18**	375 +664	**19**	534 +979	**20**	838 +693

Set 2

1 6 + 17 + 34

2 47 + 16 + 9

3 35 + 20 + 12

4 50 + 23 + 10

5 7 + 52 + 19

6 82 + 4 + 33

7 9 + 37 + 59

8 28 + 72 + 20

9 94 + 60 + 17

10 89 + 51 + 24

11 132 + 529 + 71

12 16 + 321 + 241

13 472 + 116 + 9 + 18

14 368 + 405 + 29 + 70

15 258 + 33 + 127 + 345

16 627 + 84 + 215 + 97

SUBTRACTION

First try these

Set 1

1	352 - 121	2	269 - 137	3	560 - 340	4	488 - 254
5	246 - 28	6	352 - 47	7	425 - 219	8	283 - 167
9	335 - 189	10	541 - 276	11	526 - 148	12	412 - 185
13	348 - 178	14	525 - 219	15	435 - 398	16	340 - 150
17	350 - 24	18	290 - 126	19	270 - 43	20	460 - 459

Set 2

1 48 - 25

2 54 - 38

3 127 - 63

4 197 - 104

5 212 - 185

6 342 - 176

7 195 - 40

8 350 - 227

9 391 - 296

10 240 - 113

11 473 - 205

12 406 - 158

13 561 - 370

14 603 - 208

15 349 - 149

16 653 - 250

SUBTRACTION

Now try these

Set 1

1	987 − 125	**2**	626 − 513	**3**	804 − 303	**4**	571 − 220
5	253 − 29	**6**	693 − 56	**7**	847 − 129	**8**	535 − 218
9	985 − 279	**10**	632 − 476	**11**	735 − 348	**12**	827 − 598
13	629 − 149	**14**	823 − 516	**15**	545 − 498	**16**	870 − 780
17	590 − 66	**18**	540 − 213	**19**	680 − 73	**20**	780 − 779

Set 2

1 96 − 53

2 72 − 58

3 109 − 42

4 343 − 201

5 314 − 179

6 385 − 196

7 150 − 45

8 730 − 218

9 497 − 399

10 280 − 127

11 681 − 208

12 905 − 129

13 741 − 280

14 805 − 409

15 777 − 579

16 832 − 130

PROBLEMS

First try these

Set 1

1 Add 4, 6 and 3.
2 John had 9 marbles and he won 5 more. How many had he then?
3 Mary worked 10 sums in the morning and 8 in the afternoon. How many did she work altogether?
4 In the playground there were 9 girls and 6 boys. How many children were there?
5 There were 10 cows, 2 horses and 7 sheep in a field. How many animals were in the field?
6 A postman carried 15 parcels in the morning and 8 in the afternoon. How many did he carry that day?
7 We have 12 Arithmetic books, 6 Reading books and 3 Geography books. How many books altogether?
8 There were 16 eggs in one box and 14 in another. How many eggs in the two boxes together?

Set 2

1 From 15 take 7.
2 I had 12 stamps and used 6. How many had I left?
3 Father bought 18 goldfish, but 4 of them died. How many lived?
4 Mother bought 14 kilograms of sugar and used 9 of them in making jam. How many kilograms of sugar were left over?
5 At a party children were playing with 25 balloons, and 8 of them burst. How many were left?
6 There were 36 children in a class, but 13 were away ill. How many children were present?
7 There were 29 passengers on the bus until 21 got off at the church. How many passengers were still on the bus?
8 A farmer had 30 sheep, but sold 19 at the market. How many sheep did he keep?

PROBLEMS

Now try these

Set 1

1 Add 9, 28 and 33.
2 There are 35 boys and 39 girls in a country school. How many children are there on the roll?
3 There are 47 houses on one side of the street and 26 on the other side. How many houses are there in the street?
4 There were 24 eggs in one box, 36 in a second box and 60 in a third box. How many eggs altogether in the three boxes?
5 Find the sum of 137, 76 and 5.
6 How many days are there in the last three months of the year?
7 Tom bought 50 stamps in one packet, 75 in another and 100 in a third. How many did he buy altogether?
8 A ship steamed 400 kilometres on the first day, 382 on the second and 415 on the third. How many kilometres did it travel in the three days?

Set 2

1 What must be taken from 73 to leave 28?
2 We ordered 96 bottles of lemonade for our party and we had 17 left over. How many bottles were used?
3 There were 200 people at a meeting, and 93 of these were men. How many were women?
4 Take 281 from 346.
5 Last week we used 775 bottles of milk, but this week we used 69 fewer. How many bottles have we used this week?
6 A factory made 907 bicycles last month and 823 this month. How many fewer bicycles did it make this month?
7 In a large school there are 1028 children. Of these 473 are boys. How many are girls?
8 Take two hundred and fifty-six from eight hundred and twenty-four.

MULTIPLICATION

First try these

1	4 ×2	**2**	6 ×2	**3**	9 ×2	**4**	5 ×2
5	23 ×2	**6**	41 ×2	**7**	30 ×2	**8**	14 ×2
9	16 ×2	**10**	27 ×2	**11**	45 ×2	**12**	38 ×2
13	7 ×3	**14**	2 ×3	**15**	8 ×3	**16**	0 ×3
17	25 ×3	**18**	32 ×3	**19**	46 ×3	**20**	39 ×3
21	47 ×3	**22**	30 ×3	**23**	31 ×3	**24**	23 ×3
25	4 ×4	**26**	7 ×4	**27**	0 ×4	**28**	9 ×4
29	8 ×4	**30**	2 ×4	**31**	1 ×4	**32**	3 ×4
33	15 ×4	**34**	22 ×4	**35**	37 ×4	**36**	13 ×4

MULTIPLICATION

Now try these

1   25
    ×2
___

2   12
    ×2
___

3   44
    ×2
___

4   36
    ×2
___

5   39
    ×2
___

6   48
    ×2
___

7   32
    ×2
___

8   40
    ×2
___

9   57
    ×2
___

10   64
     ×2
___

11   75
     ×2
___

12   68
     ×2
___

13   44
     ×3
___

14   26
     ×3
___

15   41
     ×3
___

16   50
     ×3
___

17   27
     ×3
___

18   52
     ×3
___

19   63
     ×3
___

20   74
     ×3
___

21   83
     ×3
___

22   90
     ×3
___

23   87
     ×3
___

24   78
     ×3
___

25   12
     ×4
___

26   21
     ×4
___

27   29
     ×4
___

28   32
     ×4
___

29   55
     ×4
___

30   76
     ×4
___

31   67
     ×4
___

32   91
     ×4
___

33   179
     ×4
___

34   150
     ×4
___

35   158
     ×4
___

36   162
     ×4
___

DIVISION

First try these

Set 1

1 2)6	**2** 2)4	**3** 2)2	**4** 2)8
5 2)22	**6** 2)46	**7** 2)62	**8** 2)48
9 2)60	**10** 2)32	**11** 2)56	**12** 2)72
13 3)9	**14** 3)0	**15** 3)6	**16** 3)3
17 3)33	**18** 3)69	**19** 3)93	**20** 3)66
21 3)45	**22** 3)51	**23** 3)78	**24** 3)72
25 4)8	**26** 4)44	**27** 4)88	**28** 4)64
29 4)52	**30** 4)68	**31** 4)76	**32** 4)92

Set 2

1 2)16	**2** 2)30	**3** 2)10	**4** 2)34
5 2)20	**6** 2)12	**7** 2)18	**8** 2)58
9 3)12	**10** 3)27	**11** 3)15	**12** 3)30
13 3)18	**14** 3)24	**15** 3)48	**16** 3)78
17 4)16	**18** 4)36	**19** 4)20	**20** 4)12
21 4)32	**22** 4)24	**23** 4)56	**24** 4)80
25 2)23	**26** 4)49	**27** 3)65	**28** 4)59
29 2)35	**30** 2)73	**31** 3)43	**32** 4)85

DIVISION

Now try these

Set 1

1 2)26	**2** 2)52	**3** 2)42	**4** 2)86
5 2)70	**6** 2)49	**7** 2)67	**8** 2)99
9 3)21	**10** 3)57	**11** 3)29	**12** 3)70
13 3)41	**14** 3)68	**15** 3)91	**16** 3)63
17 3)19	**18** 3)31	**19** 3)80	**20** 3)86
21 4)58	**22** 4)90	**23** 4)18	**24** 4)10
25 4)81	**26** 4)61	**27** 4)29	**28** 4)78
29 4)30	**30** 4)17	**31** 4)97	**32** 4)50

Set 2

1 2)248	**2** 2)462	**3** 2)628	**4** 2)406
5 3)396	**6** 3)690	**7** 3)963	**8** 3)309
9 4)484	**10** 4)804	**11** 4)800	**12** 4)408
13 2)427	**14** 2)526	**15** 2)438	**16** 2)537
17 2)175	**18** 2)106	**19** 2)207	**20** 3)523
21 3)423	**22** 3)375	**23** 3)249	**24** 3)165
25 3)905	**26** 4)364	**27** 4)128	**28** 4)206
29 4)528	**30** 4)876	**31** 4)935	**32** 4)700

PROBLEMS

First try these

Set 1

1 Multiply twenty-five by three.
2 How many tyres do we need for 48 bicycles?
3 If Mary saves 4 pennies each day for 28 days, how many pennies will she save altogether?
4 How many legs do we need for 12 three-legged stools?
5 Multiply eleven by three, and add 6 to your answer.
6 A boy wrote the word SHIP ten times. How many letters did he write?
7 There are 4 boxes and each holds 24 chocolates. How many chocolates are there altogether?
8 Each girl in a class is given 3 exercise books. If there are 29 girls, how many books are needed?
9 Multiply 9 by 3. Take 16 away from your answer.

Set 2

1 How many times does 4 divide into 28?
2 Fifty-two children were lined up in 4 equal rows. How many children were in each row?
3 Share 27 sweets equally among 3 girls.
4 Seventy-four books were put into 2 equal piles. How many books in each pile?
5 Share 50 stamps equally among 3 boys. How many will each get, and how many will be left over?
6 Divide 96 by 2. Take the answer from 50.
7 In a class of 38 children there are equal numbers of boys and girls. How many girls are there in the class?
8 Divide 43 oranges among 3 boys. How many will each get, and how many will be left over?
9 Ninety pennies are to be shared equally between two children. How many pennies are given to each child?

PROBLEMS

Now try these

Set 1

1 Multiply ninety-five by three.
2 A train travels at 110 kilometres per hour. How many kilometres will it travel in 4 hours?
3 How many eggs are there in 3 boxes, if each box holds 12 dozen eggs?
4 Multiply one hundred and sixty-nine by two. Take the result from 500.
5 One hundred centimetres measures the same distance as one metre. How many centimetres measures the same distance as 3 metres 10 centimetres?
6 Each child paid 30 pennies to visit a model railway. If 4 children visited the railway, how many pennies were paid altogether?
7 A racing car travels 290 kilometres in one hour. How far will it go in 2 hours?
8 A ship steams 396 kilometres in a day. How far will it go in 4 days?

Set 2

1 Find how many threes there are in one hundred and thirty-five.
2 A racing car travelled 560 kilometres in 4 hours. If it went at a steady speed, how far did it travel in 1 hour?
3 Divide 598 by 2. Take the answer from 750.
4 Share 400 nuts among 3 children so that each has as many as possible. How many would each get and how many would be left over?
5 We bought 650 cakes for a party so that each child could have two. How many children were at the party?
6 A ship steamed 1200 kilometres in 3 days at a steady speed. How many kilometres did it go each day?
7 Divide 852 by 4, and add your answer to 25.
8 Share 175 pennies among 3 boys. How many pennies does each get, and how many are left over?

MULTIPLICATION

First try these

1   3
      ×5
	2 6
	      ×5
		3 4
		      ×5
			4 0
			      ×5

5   2
      ×5
	6 5
	      ×5
		7 1
		      ×5
			8 10
			      ×5

9   7
      ×5
	10 31
	      ×5
		11 22
		      ×5
			12 43
			      ×5

13   2
     ×10
	14 6
	     ×10
		15 1
		     ×10
			16 9
			     ×10

17   0
     ×10
	18 5
	     ×10
		19 3
		     ×10
			20 8
			     ×10

21   27
     ×10
	22 16
	     ×10
		23 24
		     ×10
			24 33
			     ×10

25   7
     ×11
	26 0
	     ×11
		27 9
		     ×11
			28 1
			     ×11

29   8
     ×11
	30 2
	     ×11
		31 5
		     ×11
			32 6
			     ×11

33   3
     ×11
	34 12
	     ×11
		35 15
		     ×11
			36 26
			     ×11

MULTIPLICATION

Now try these

1   25
     × 5
	2 38
	     × 5
		3 52
		     × 5
			4 71
			     × 5

5   84
     × 5
	6 67
	     × 5
		7 40
		     × 5
			8 93
			     × 5

9   46
     × 5
	10 89
	     × 5
		11 98
		     × 5
			12 77
			     × 5

13   29
     × 10
	14 48
	     × 10
		15 70
		     × 10
			16 61
			     × 10

17   96
     × 10
	18 85
	     × 10
		19 54
		     × 10
			20 42
			     × 10

21   123
     × 10
	22 167
	     × 10
		23 194
		     × 10
			24 203
			     × 10

25   78
     × 11
	26 50
	     × 11
		27 39
		     × 11
			28 96
			     × 11

29   84
     × 11
	30 92
	     × 11
		31 61
		     × 11
			32 152
			     × 11

33   120
     × 11
	34 143
	     × 11
		35 117
		     × 11
			36 138
			     × 11

DIVISION

First try these

Set 1

1 5)25	**2** 5)40	**3** 5)30	**4** 5)10
5 5)45	**6** 5)20	**7** 5)15	**8** 5)75
9 5)90	**10** 5)65	**11** 5)85	**12** 5)60
13 10)80	**14** 10)20	**15** 10)60	**16** 10)110
17 10)150	**18** 10)70	**19** 10)190	**20** 10)220
21 10)160	**22** 10)270	**23** 10)100	**24** 10)250
25 11)33	**26** 11)66	**27** 11)99	**28** 11)132
29 11)44	**30** 11)55	**31** 11)110	**32** 11)77

Set 2

1 5)37	**2** 5)80	**3** 5)76	**4** 5)68
5 5)29	**6** 5)125	**7** 5)100	**8** 5)141
9 5)137	**10** 5)184	**11** 5)206	**12** 5)189
13 10)190	**14** 10)268	**15** 10)123	**16** 10)240
17 10)176	**18** 10)105	**19** 10)284	**20** 10)312
21 11)34	**22** 11)70	**23** 11)56	**24** 11)127
25 11)100	**26** 11)82	**27** 11)49	**28** 11)104
29 11)135	**30** 11)149	**31** 11)180	**32** 11)201

DIVISION

Now try these

Set 1

1 5)70	**2** 5)95	**3** 5)105	**4** 5)195
5 5)240	**6** 5)380	**7** 5)570	**8** 5)465
9 5)825	**10** 5)775	**11** 5)625	**12** 5)995
13 10)130	**14** 10)560	**15** 10)820	**16** 10)700
17 10)860	**18** 10)950	**19** 10)1100	**20** 10)1250
21 11)143	**22** 11)198	**23** 11)484	**24** 11)352
25 11)231	**26** 11)792	**27** 11)836	**28** 11)913
29 11)990	**30** 11)869	**31** 11)1100	**32** 11)1001

Set 2

1 5)46	**2** 5)52	**3** 5)88	**4** 5)39
5 5)187	**6** 5)106	**7** 5)302	**8** 5)938
9 5)882	**10** 5)1056	**11** 5)1247	**12** 5)1005
13 10)489	**14** 10)765	**15** 10)951	**16** 10)637
17 10)1340	**18** 10)1074	**19** 10)1553	**20** 10)1906
21 11)876	**22** 11)706	**23** 11)900	**24** 11)1020
25 11)1101	**26** 11)1302	**27** 11)989	**28** 11)1980
29 11)1345	**30** 11)1752	**31** 11)2070	**32** 11)2464

PROBLEMS

First try these

Set 1

1 A child reads 6 pages of his reading book each day. How many pages will he read in 5 days?
2 We planted 7 apple trees in each row. How many trees will there be in 11 rows?
3 Take 4 × 5 from 22.
4 There are 12 stamps in a row. If I buy a sheet of 11 rows, how many stamps will I get?
5 Multiply 7 by 10. Take 16 from your answer.
6 How many needles are there in 16 packets, if there are 10 needles in every packet?
7 In our school there are 11 classrooms, with 23 desks in each. How many desks in the school?
8 How many pencils are there in 10 boxes, if each box holds two dozen pencils?

Set 2

1 How many journeys must a boy make to move 48 kilograms of sand packed into 8 kilogram bags?
2 How many times will 11 divide into 60, and what is left over?
3 Two numbers multiplied together give 75. If one of these numbers is 5, what is the other?
4 If a lorry travels 280 kilometres in 5 hours, and goes at a steady speed, how many kilometres does it travel in 1 hour?
5 At a party, 125 sweets were shared equally among 10 children. How many did each child get? How many were left over?
6 Share 190 foreign stamps equally among 10 friends.
7 Place 72 books in 5 piles, so that each pile has the same number of books in it. How many books will there be in each pile, and how many will be left over?
8 Divide 247 by 11. What is left over?

PROBLEMS

Now try these

Set 1

1 A newspaper has 8 sheets. How many sheets in 11 papers?

2 Find the sum of 6 × 10 and 14 × 5.

3 A book has 11 chapters, and there are 28 pages to each chapter. How many pages are in the book?

4 A train is made up of 10 carriages, and there are 48 people in each carriage. How many people are there in the train?

5 A milkman can deliver 120 bottles of milk in an hour. How many can he deliver in 5 hours?

6 In a box there are 96 bars of chocolate. How many bars are there in 10 boxes?

7 How many cigarettes are there in 144 packets, each of which holds 10?

8 We motored 240 kilometres a day for 5 days. How many kilometres did we travel altogether?

Set 2

1 How many times does 11 divide into 100, and what is left over?

2 How many wooden posts, each 2 metres high, can be cut from 197 metres of timber?

3 How many groups of 10 counters can I make from 670 counters?

4 In a large park there were 88 boys playing in football matches, with 11 on each side. How many matches were being played?

5 Divide 1250 by 5.

6 There are 242 words on the page of a book and 11 words on each line. How many lines are there?

7 If 317 children are divided into 5 equal groups, how many will there be in each group, and how many are left over?

8 Divide 923 by 10. What is left over?

MULTIPLICATION

First try these

1   8
×6

2   2
×6

3   5
×6

4   0
×6

5   9
×6

6   7
×6

7   1
×6

8 15
×6

9 21
×6

10 30
×6

11 24
×6

12 42
×6

13   8
×8

14   5
×8

15   2
×8

16   7
×8

17 10
×8

18   0
×8

19 11
×8

20 14
×8

21 19
×8

22 46
×8

23 32
×8

24 41
×8

25   7
×12

26   2
×12

27   0
×12

28   8
×12

29   5
×12

30 10
×12

31 19
×12

32 16
×12

33 38
×12

34 34
×12

35 46
×12

36 50
×12

MULTIPLICATION

Now try these

1	11 ×6	**2**	16 ×6	**3**	13 ×6	**4**	19 ×6
5	28 ×6	**6**	40 ×6	**7**	52 ×6	**8**	45 ×6
9	63 ×6	**10**	98 ×6	**11**	54 ×6	**12**	77 ×6
13	13 ×8	**14**	21 ×8	**15**	15 ×8	**16**	36 ×8
17	49 ×8	**18**	24 ×8	**19**	78 ×8	**20**	57 ×8
21	62 ×8	**22**	95 ×8	**23**	83 ×8	**24**	171 ×8
25	9 ×12	**26**	14 ×12	**27**	22 ×12	**28**	11 ×12
29	28 ×12	**30**	63 ×12	**31**	47 ×12	**32**	84 ×12
33	79 ×12	**34**	92 ×12	**35**	68 ×12	**36**	56 ×12

DIVISION

First try these

Set 1

1	6)12	**2**	6)30	**3**	6)0	**4**	6)42
5	6)6	**6**	6)18	**7**	6)48	**8**	6)60
9	6)54	**10**	6)84	**11**	6)102	**12**	6)120
13	8)24	**14**	8)40	**15**	8)16	**16**	8)0
17	8)72	**18**	8)96	**19**	8)104	**20**	8)128
21	8)160	**22**	8)152	**23**	8)176	**24**	8)248
25	12)60	**26**	12)36	**27**	12)108	**28**	12)48
29	12)120	**30**	12)156	**31**	12)240	**32**	12)180

Set 2

1	6)19	**2**	6)28	**3**	6)61	**4**	6)47
5	6)39	**6**	6)85	**7**	6)105	**8**	6)116
9	8)25	**10**	8)37	**11**	8)68	**12**	8)50
13	8)43	**14**	8)78	**15**	8)83	**16**	8)94
17	8)106	**18**	8)195	**19**	8)201	**20**	8)258
21	12)40	**22**	12)63	**23**	12)35	**24**	12)99
25	12)126	**26**	12)150	**27**	12)189	**28**	12)253
29	12)295	**30**	12)241	**31**	12)268	**32**	12)202

DIVISION

Now try these

Set 1

1 6)36	**2** 6)66	**3** 6)180	**4** 6)114
5 6)210	**6** 6)486	**7** 6)312	**8** 6)258
9 6)564	**10** 6)606	**11** 6)984	**12** 6)1080
13 8)56	**14** 8)80	**15** 8)144	**16** 8)272
17 8)504	**18** 8)632	**19** 8)976	**20** 8)808
21 8)1120	**22** 8)1376	**23** 8)1728	**24** 8)2000
25 12)96	**26** 12)132	**27** 12)192	**28** 12)516
29 12)408	**30** 12)828	**31** 12)624	**32** 12)1428

Set 2

1 6)87	**2** 6)53	**3** 6)100	**4** 6)131
5 6)361	**6** 6)497	**7** 6)742	**8** 6)1004
9 8)70	**10** 8)107	**11** 8)59	**12** 8)123
13 8)162	**14** 8)508	**15** 8)395	**16** 8)431
17 8)666	**18** 8)931	**19** 8)1549	**20** 8)1723
21 12)136	**22** 12)95	**23** 12)160	**24** 12)259
25 12)368	**26** 12)747	**27** 12)602	**28** 12)958
29 12)1279	**30** 12)1653	**31** 12)2057	**32** 12)2943

PROBLEMS

First try these

Set 1

1 Eight boys were each given 6 pennies. How many pennies were they given altogether?
2 A dozen bars of soap are packed in a box. How many bars are there in 5 boxes?
3 If a lift can carry 8 people at a time, how many people could it carry on 4 journeys?
4 In one packet there are 6 crayons. How many crayons are there in 10 packets?
5 Three fisherman each caught 12 fish. How many did they catch altogether?
6 A taxi can carry 6 people. How many people can 7 taxis carry?
7 In an orchard, apple trees are planted 12 in a row. If there are 10 rows, how many trees in the orchard?
8 How many weekdays are there in 26 weeks?

Set 2

1 At a party, 30 children sat in 6 equal rows. How many children in each row?
2 Ninety-six toys were packed in 8 boxes, so that there were the same number in each box. How many toys were there in each box?
3 How many lengths of rope, each 4 metres long, can be cut from a rope 84 metres long?
4 Divide 64 by 8. Add 2 to your answer.
5 Seventy-two litres of water flow from a pipe in 6 minutes. How much flows in 1 minute?
6 How many dozen eggs are there in a box holding 132 eggs?
7 How many times does 6 divide into 101? What is left over?
8 Share 150 pennies equally among 12 girls. How many will each girl have, and how many pennies will be left over?

PROBLEMS

Now try these

Set 1

1 There are 10 houses in a terrace and 6 people live in each house. How many people live in the terrace?
2 How many people can travel in 6 buses, if each bus takes 52 passengers?
3 There are 11 windows in each of 8 houses. How many windows are there altogether?
4 How many soldiers live in 32 tents, if there are 12 men to every tent?
5 There are 60 minutes in 1 hour. How many minutes are there in 8 hours?
6 How many bars of chocolate are there in 48 boxes, if each box holds 1 dozen bars?
7 Multiply 19 by 8. Take the answer from 13×12.
8 How many herrings are there in 1 dozen boxes, if there are 96 herrings in a box?

Set 2

1 Place 84 bricks in 6 equal piles. How many will there be in each pile?
2 A gardener has 192 plum trees which are to be planted in 12 equal rows. How many trees will there be in each row?
3 There are 12 coins in each bag. How many bags are needed for 228 coins?
4 A boy had 652 marbles. He kept 28 and shared the rest equally among 8 friends. How many did each get?
5 How many groups of 6 can be made from 923, and how many units will be left over?
6 How many boxes of eggs, each holding 1 dozen, can be packed from 1079 eggs, and how many eggs will be left over?
7 Divide 846 by 6. Then divide 200 by 8. Add your two answers together.

MULTIPLICATION

First try these

1   6
     ×7
———

2   2
     ×7
———

3   4
     ×7
———

4   7
     ×7
———

5   0
     ×7
———

6   8
     ×7
———

7   1
     ×7
———

8   10
     ×7
———

9   3
     ×7
———

10   11
      ×7
———

11   15
      ×7
———

12   19
      ×7
———

13   24
      ×7
———

14   36
      ×7
———

15   27
      ×7
———

16   13
      ×7
———

17   38
      ×7
———

18   45
      ×7
———

19   51
      ×7
———

20   29
      ×7
———

21   9
      ×9
———

22   4
      ×9
———

23   5
      ×9
———

24   0
      ×9
———

25   11
      ×9
———

26   7
      ×9
———

27   2
      ×9
———

28   3
      ×9
———

29   6
      ×9
———

30   12
      ×9
———

31   10
      ×9
———

32   15
      ×9
———

33   24
      ×9
———

34   30
      ×9
———

35   27
      ×9
———

36   13
      ×9
———

MULTIPLICATION

Now try these

1 9 ×7	**2** 12 ×7	**3** 20 ×7	**4** 31 ×7
5 17 ×7	**6** 26 ×7	**7** 35 ×7	**8** 54 ×7
9 48 ×7	**10** 79 ×7	**11** 82 ×7	**12** 90 ×7
13 57 ×7	**14** 49 ×7	**15** 94 ×7	**16** 76 ×7
17 85 ×7	**18** 151 ×7	**19** 99 ×7	**20** 145 ×7
21 8 ×9	**22** 16 ×9	**23** 19 ×9	**24** 25 ×9
25 14 ×9	**26** 23 ×9	**27** 56 ×9	**28** 40 ×9
29 61 ×9	**30** 82 ×9	**31** 69 ×9	**32** 75 ×9
33 86 ×9	**34** 47 ×9	**35** 63 ×9	**36** 72 ×9

DIVISION

First try these

Set 1

1 7)21	**2** 7)42	**3** 7)0	**4** 7)14
5 7)63	**6** 7)28	**7** 7)7	**8** 7)70
9 7)56	**10** 7)98	**11** 7)119	**12** 7)175
13 7)133	**14** 7)189	**15** 7)231	**16** 7)252
17 9)36	**18** 9)9	**19** 9)54	**20** 9)81
21 9)0	**22** 9)18	**23** 9)63	**24** 9)90
25 9)45	**26** 9)108	**27** 9)144	**28** 9)189
29 9)207	**30** 9)162	**31** 9)234	**32** 9)270

Set 2

1 7)37	**2** 7)54	**3** 7)20	**4** 7)41
5 7)18	**6** 7)58	**7** 7)75	**8** 7)91
9 7)107	**10** 7)85	**11** 7)114	**12** 7)187
13 7)161	**14** 7)197	**15** 7)210	**16** 7)234
17 9)20	**18** 9)37	**19** 9)29	**20** 9)48
21 9)56	**22** 9)82	**23** 9)72	**24** 9)106
25 9)165	**26** 9)147	**27** 9)186	**28** 9)152
29 9)174	**30** 9)200	**31** 9)215	**32** 9)229

DIVISION

Now try these

Set 1

1 7)49	**2** 7)84	**3** 7)35	**4** 7)77
5 7)126	**6** 7)168	**7** 7)196	**8** 7)259
9 7)371	**10** 7)742	**11** 7)357	**12** 7)504
13 7)434	**14** 7)693	**15** 7)980	**16** 7)1155
17 9)72	**18** 9)27	**19** 9)117	**20** 9)99
21 9)180	**22** 9)135	**23** 9)198	**24** 9)279
25 9)333	**26** 9)495	**27** 9)576	**28** 9)711
29 9)684	**30** 9)972	**31** 9)1431	**32** 9)1080

Set 2

1 7)53	**2** 7)79	**3** 7)60	**4** 7)97
5 7)109	**6** 7)129	**7** 7)147	**8** 7)186
9 7)213	**10** 7)489	**11** 7)593	**12** 7)839
13 7)906	**14** 7)1395	**15** 7)1207	**16** 7)1000
17 9)23	**18** 9)40	**19** 9)87	**20** 9)103
21 9)163	**22** 9)155	**23** 9)298	**24** 9)217
25 9)427	**26** 9)835	**27** 9)726	**28** 9)809
29 9)673	**30** 9)1427	**31** 9)2017	**32** 9)2539

PROBLEMS

First try these

Set 1

1 Multiply 7 by 8.
2 There are 9 panes of glass in each of 9 sheds. How many panes of glass are there altogether?
3 In a classroom, there are 3 rows of girls with 9 in a row, and 4 rows of boys with 7 in a row. How many children are there in the class?
4 Multiply 12 by 7. Take 4 from the answer.
5 How many sweets do I need to give 9 boys 4 sweets each?
6 Seven boys were each given 7 oranges. What was the total number of oranges given away?
7 If there are 9 hair-clips on a card, how many hair-clips are there on a dozen cards?
8 If a crate holds 35 bottles of milk, how many bottles do 9 crates hold?

Set 2

1 Share 21 toys equally among 7 children. How many will each get?
2 Tom had 70 marbles. He gave away 7 and divided the rest equally among 9 friends. How many did each friend get?
3 How many times does 9 divide into 86? What is left over?
4 Divide 46 apples equally among 7 children. How many will each have, and how many will be left over?
5 Eighty-four lettuces were packed into 7 boxes of the same size. How many were packed in each box?
6 We bought 144 trees, which are to be planted 9 in a row. How many rows will there be?
7 A girl can carry 7 bricks. How many complete journeys will she have to make to move 112 bricks?
8 How many times does 7 divide into 160? What is left over?

PROBLEMS

Now try these

Set 1

1 If a boiler burns 11 kilograms of coke every day, how many kilograms will it burn in a week?

2 How far would a cyclist travel in 9 hours, if his speed is 15 kilometres per hour?

3 Multiply 102 by 7.

4 If 9 boxes each weigh 84 kilograms, how many kilograms do they weigh altogether?

5 The distance round a field is 220 metres. If I walked round the field 9 times, how many metres would I walk?

6 How many days are there in 208 weeks?

7 A man sets off on a motor tour of 1000 kilometres. If he travels 75 kilometres each day, for 9 days, how much further has he still to go?

8 Multiply 326 by 7.

Set 2

1 Share 39 books equally among 7 boys. How many books does each boy get, and how many books will be left over?

2 How many times does 9 divide into 169, and what is the remainder?

3 If 196 kilograms of biscuits were shared equally among 7 shops, how many kilograms would each have?

4 Nine men are to carry 180 kilograms of luggage between them. Each man is to carry the same amount. How much will this be?

5 A car travelled at a steady speed and covered 448 kilometres in 7 hours. How far did it travel each hour?

6 Find the difference between 98 divided by 7, and 126 divided by 9.

7 How many times does 9 divide into 316? What is the remainder?

8 How many times does 7 divide into 496? How many are left over?

FURTHER ADDITION AND SUBTRACTION

First try these

Set 1

1 17 + 9 + 108	**10** 49 + 13 + 109 + 200
2 26 + 52 + 97	**11** 418 + 123 + 14 + 7
3 48 + 16 + 250	**12** 373 + 65 + 13 + 115
4 37 + 128 + 291	**13** 73 + 208 + 89 + 16
5 65 + 27 + 498	**14** 245 + 27 + 138 + 50
6 298 + 365 + 251	**15** 193 + 59 + 54 + 128
7 307 + 18 + 111	**16** 8 + 32 + 410 + 12
8 176 + 19 + 84	**17** 437 + 61 + 215 + 173
9 268 + 132 + 69	**18** 82 + 195 + 500 + 7

Set 2

1 53 – 29	**10** 40 + 97 – 61
2 84 – 67	**11** 84 + 128 – 76
3 123 – 64	**12** 190 + 49 – 103
4 196 – 138	**13** 176 + 241 – 292
5 307 – 195	**14** 282 + 139 – 155
6 246 – 178	**15** 348 + 297 – 160
7 485 – 297	**16** 438 + 217 – 388
8 600 – 527	**17** 519 + 360 – 495
9 750 – 368	**18** 528 + 173 – 419

FURTHER ADDITION AND SUBTRACTION

Now try these

Set 1

1 709 + 116 + 140

2 169 + 8 + 574

3 134 + 19 + 257

4 248 + 100 + 125

5 692 + 208 + 476

6 357 + 240 + 943

7 326 + 142 + 850

8 128 + 776 + 391

9 417 + 633 + 747

10 645 + 172 + 352 + 18

11 433 + 830 + 121 + 97

12 235 + 413 + 12 + 251

13 634 + 243 + 532 + 80

14 73 + 900 + 46 + 168

15 356 + 349 + 19 + 207

16 155 + 436 + 725 + 798

17 845 + 93 + 137 + 354

18 801 + 29 + 8 + 937

Set 2

1 427 − 139

2 620 − 475

3 986 − 231

4 807 − 144

5 785 − 697

6 532 − 409

7 391 − 286

8 768 − 138

9 287 − 99

10 192 + 365 − 217

11 405 + 301 − 188

12 327 + 509 − 653

13 718 + 507 − 472

14 175 + 488 − 236

15 283 + 569 − 708

16 286 − 195 + 322

17 528 − 365 + 74

18 69 + 820 − 250

MULTIPLICATION AND DIVISION

First try these

Set 1

1 5 × 3	**2** 23 × 3	**3** 14 × 4
4 21 × 6	**5** 33 × 5	**6** 37 × 8
7 49 × 7	**8** 123 × 3	**9** 115 × 3
10 172 × 4	**11** 126 × 2	**12** 243 × 3
13 212 × 5	**14** 131 × 9	**15** 107 × 8
16 211 × 9	**17** 225 × 4	**18** 289 × 4
19 378 × 3	**20** 238 × 7	**21** 610 × 10
22 500 × 12	**23** 401 × 10	**24** 893 × 4

Set 2

1 3)9	**2** 5)11	**3** 4)87	**4** 4)92
5 7)14	**6** 6)31	**7** 5)107	**8** 6)126
9 12)36	**10** 11)59	**11** 9)98	**12** 10)101
13 9)72	**14** 12)148	**15** 8)169	**16** 11)331
17 2)246	**18** 3)639	**19** 6)608	**20** 5)725
21 6)785	**22** 3)621	**23** 4)343	**24** 7)690
25 9)981	**26** 8)664	**27** 10)823	**28** 9)815
29 12)156	**30** 11)295	**31** 12)610	**32** 9)728

MULTIPLICATION AND DIVISION

Now try these

Set 1

1 17×4	**2** 24×2	**3** 13×6
4 126×3	**5** 172×3	**6** 29×5
7 42×11	**8** 71×12	**9** 121×3
10 101×9	**11** 120×4	**12** 322×6
13 175×10	**14** 604×4	**15** 290×8
16 407×3	**17** 709×7	**18** 765×10
19 689×8	**20** 431×12	**21** 920×7
22 806×9	**23** 482×9	**24** 840×11

Set 2

1 $9)\overline{27}$	**2** $11)\overline{89}$	**3** $6)\overline{69}$	**4** $8)\overline{136}$
5 $11)\overline{220}$	**6** $12)\overline{361}$	**7** $10)\overline{520}$	**8** $9)\overline{463}$
9 $6)\overline{268}$	**10** $8)\overline{513}$	**11** $7)\overline{708}$	**12** $12)\overline{493}$
13 $12)\overline{527}$	**14** $10)\overline{697}$	**15** $11)\overline{895}$	**16** $8)\overline{817}$
17 $11)\overline{552}$	**18** $9)\overline{798}$	**19** $10)\overline{832}$	**20** $8)\overline{938}$
21 $8)\overline{1071}$	**22** $7)\overline{1400}$	**23** $12)\overline{1335}$	**24** $9)\overline{1212}$
25 $12)\overline{1476}$	**26** $6)\overline{2412}$	**27** $9)\overline{1809}$	**28** $11)\overline{2591}$
29 $12)\overline{2472}$	**30** $11)\overline{1020}$	**31** $9)\overline{1515}$	**32** $10)\overline{1172}$

GENERAL REVISION

First try these

Add

1	23	**2**	64	**3**	129	**4**	106
	5		32		+86		+329
	+9		+1		——		——
	——		——				

Subtract

5	42	**6**	80	**7**	419	**8**	384
	−17		−26		−205		−78
	——		——		——		——

Multiply

9	13	**10**	19	**11**	27	**12**	41
	×6		×8		×11		×9
	——		——		——		——

Divide

13 4)39   **14** 6)93   **15** 12)150   **16** 8)89

17 A party of 63 children went to the country and 47 to the seaside. How many went away altogether?

18 A train is 102 metres long and the station platform is 68 metres long. How much of the train is outside the platform?

19 A grocer sold 87 kilograms of biscuits in 3 days. How many kilograms did he sell daily, if he sold the same weight of biscuits each day?

20 A milkman sells 2 dozen eggs in a certain road each day. How many eggs will he sell in that road in 5 days?

21 From five hundred and six take one hundred and nine.

22 Tulips are made up into bunches of 8. How many bunches could be made from 152 tulips?

23 There are 7 rows of tins and 96 tins in a row. How many tins are there altogether?

24 A boy had 34 conkers. He lost 7 and then found 13 more. How many did he have then?

GENERAL REVISION

Now try these

Add

1	195 207 +2	2	58 226 +14	3	792 +385	4	692 +413

Subtract

5	83 −24	6	110 −72	7	317 −254	8	584 −389

Multiply

9	30 ×12	10	45 ×9	11	128 ×7	12	253 ×6

Divide

13 5)70   14 11)138   15 7)308   16 9)1531

17 A weaver made 3 metres of cloth every hour. How many metres did he make in a week, if he worked for 54 hours?

18 Out of 6 dozen oranges, 3 score were sold. How many oranges were left?

19 How many electric lights are there in a street of 74 houses, if there are 11 lights in each house?

20 Eight dolls cost 656 pence altogether. If they were all the same price, how many pence did each doll cost?

21 A shopkeeper had 2 gross of oranges. If 39 were bad, how many could he sell?

22 Divide 895 by 12.

23 Add together one hundred, and two hundred and six. Add nine times nine to your answer.

24 Tom has 3 bags each holding 120 marbles. John has 5 bags each holding 48 marbles. How many more has Tom than John?

MONEY ADDITION

First try these

1 p 03 +02	**2** p 05 +04	**3** p 07 +03	**4** p 06 +06
5 p 09 +02	**6** p 10 +10	**7** p 08 +11	**8** p 03 +19
9 p 14 +12	**10** p 17 +10	**11** p 13 +13	**12** p 25 +10
13 p 28 +04	**14** p 16 +17	**15** p 09 +14	**16** p 18 +13
17 p 35 +05	**18** p 47 +03	**19** p 39 +21	**20** p 56 +12
21 p 30 $+18\frac{1}{2}$	**22** p $16\frac{1}{2}$ $+41\frac{1}{2}$	**23** p 27 +25	**24** p 40 $+20\frac{1}{2}$
25 p $54\frac{1}{2}$ +15	**26** p 27 +21	**27** p $29\frac{1}{2}$ $+32\frac{1}{2}$	**28** p $57\frac{1}{2}$ $+23\frac{1}{2}$

MONEY ADDITION

Now try these

Set 1

	p		p		p		p
1	14	**2**	16	**3**	05	**4**	11
	+03		+02		+10		+08

	p		p		p		p
5	15	**6**	06	**7**	17	**8**	10
	+07		+18		+09		+19

	p		p		p		p
9	14	**10**	25	**11**	38	**12**	21
	+14		+08		+06		+29

	p		p		p		p
13	$36\frac{1}{2}$	**14**	54	**15**	27	**16**	$64\frac{1}{2}$
	$+16\frac{1}{2}$		$+08\frac{1}{2}$		+43		$+20\frac{1}{2}$

	p		p		p		p
17	50	**18**	$48\frac{1}{2}$	**19**	19	**20**	65
	+27		$+34\frac{1}{2}$		$+57\frac{1}{2}$		+29

	p		p		p		p
21	$37\frac{1}{2}$	**22**	54	**23**	71	**24**	$53\frac{1}{2}$
	+56		+45		+19		$+28\frac{1}{2}$

Set 2

1 02p +04p +06p

2 $05\frac{1}{2}$p +$03\frac{1}{2}$p +$10\frac{1}{2}$p

3 11p +13p +12p

4 $20\frac{1}{2}$p +$17\frac{1}{2}$p +13p

5 15p +07p +29p

6 $24\frac{1}{2}$p +18p +$20\frac{1}{2}$p

7 39p +46p +01p

8 $48\frac{1}{2}$p +$19\frac{1}{2}$p +31p

MONEY SUBTRACTION

First try these

1
  p
27
– 04
_____

2
  p
18
– 03
_____

3
  p
29
– 06
_____

4
  p
37
– 07
_____

5
  p
36
– 05
_____

6
  p
49
– 09
_____

7
  p
56
– 02
_____

8
  p
25
– 14
_____

9
  p
44
– 23
_____

10
  p
58
– 12
_____

11
  p
67
– 47
_____

12
  p
75
– 30
_____

13
  p
$99\frac{1}{2}$
– 11
_____

14
  p
80
– 50
_____

15
  p
29
– $16\frac{1}{2}$
_____

16
  p
$58\frac{1}{2}$
– 44
_____

17
  p
78
– $70\frac{1}{2}$
_____

18
  p
35
– 08
_____

19
  p
$43\frac{1}{2}$
– $09\frac{1}{2}$
_____

20
  p
$90\frac{1}{2}$
– 03
_____

21
  p
66
– 07
_____

22
  p
$42\frac{1}{2}$
– 26
_____

23
  p
64
– $39\frac{1}{2}$
_____

24
  p
$91\frac{1}{2}$
– $14\frac{1}{2}$
_____

25
  p
75
– $18\frac{1}{2}$
_____

26
  p
$83\frac{1}{2}$
– $67\frac{1}{2}$
_____

27
  p
98
– 89
_____

28
  p
92
– $46\frac{1}{2}$
_____

MONEY SUBTRACTION

Now try these

Set 1

1	p	2	p	3	p	4	p
	67		58		79		45
	− 07		− 03		− 08		− 04

5	p	6	p	7	p	8	p
	46		53		88		90
	− 25		− 11		− 32		− 20

9	p	10	p	11	p	12	p
	$69\frac{1}{2}$		97		55		$94\frac{1}{2}$
	− 54		− $26\frac{1}{2}$		− 40		− $08\frac{1}{2}$

13	p	14	p	15	p	16	p
	52		66		$87\frac{1}{2}$		70
	− 05		− $09\frac{1}{2}$		− 08		− 06

Set 2

1 42p − 29p

2 50p − 48p

3 91p − $30\frac{1}{2}$p

4 64p − 17p

5 95p − 45p

6 $73\frac{1}{2}$p − $28\frac{1}{2}$p

7 56p − 51p

8 $37\frac{1}{2}$p − 29p

9 48p − 19p

10 63p − 27p

11 94p − 66p

12 85p − 38p

13 97p − $34\frac{1}{2}$p

14 75p − 27p

15 80p − $56\frac{1}{2}$p

16 90p − $81\frac{1}{2}$p

MONEY PROBLEMS

First try these

Set 1

1 Mary bought two small toys. One cost 9p and the other 14p. How much money did she spend altogether?

2 John had 15p and Tom gave him 13p. How much money did John have then?

3 Add $7\frac{1}{2}$p to 17p.

4 Susan was given 9p, Anne 7p and Joan 5p. What was the total amount given away?

5 Find the sum of $19\frac{1}{2}$p, $2\frac{1}{2}$p and 8p.

6 Father spent 28p on sweets and 32p on papers. How much did he spend altogether?

7 Add together 24p and 12p.

8 A girl spent 30p on sweets one week and 15p the next. How much money did she spend on sweets in the two weeks?

9 I bought bread costing 36p and cakes costing $39\frac{1}{2}$p. What was the total cost of these articles?

Set 2

1 Tom has 10p and George has 4p less. How much money has George?

2 Take 13p from 28p.

3 Kate spent $11\frac{1}{2}$p. How much change did she have from 50p?

4 Mary earned 25p and Jack earned 41p. How much more money did Jack earn than Mary?

5 What must be added to $22\frac{1}{2}$p to make 37p?

6 In one week I spent $18\frac{1}{2}$p and the next week 39p. How much more money did I spend in the second week?

7 A boy has $6\frac{1}{2}$p. How much more must he save in order to have 40p?

8 Add 9p to 7p, and take your answer from 53p.

9 Find the difference between 8p and 31p.

MONEY PROBLEMS

Now try these

Set 1

1 I bought a book costing 65p and a pencil costing 7p. How much did I spend altogether?
2 Add 16p, 27p and 43½p.
3 On Monday John spent 24p on ice-cream, 25p on sweets and 22p on newspapers. How much money did he spend that day?
4 Jack bought articles costing 5p, 17½p, 26p and 9p. How much did he spend?
5 Find the sum of 12½p, 24½p and 30p.
6 Janet bought a toy costing 21½p and a book costing 75p. What was the total cost of these two articles?
7 Add 14p, 11½p and 50p.
8 To a half of 50p add a half of 40p.
9 Add 43½p to one-half of 90p.

Set 2

1 If I buy 3 ice-creams each costing 18p, how much change shall I have from 60p?
2 Anne has 7½p but she needs 40p. How much more money must she save?
3 What is the difference in price between a toy costing 42p and one costing 70p?
4 I started the day with 48p. After spending 15p and 20p, how much money had I left?
5 Mother paid 28½p for soap. How much change did she have from 40p?
6 Take 17½p from 65p.
7 John earned 40p, but Tom earned only 16p. How much more money did John earn than Tom?
8 Find the difference between 89p and 27½p.

MONEY ADDITION

First try these

1 £
0·03
+0·15

2 £
0·11
+0·24

3 £
0·36
+0·40

4 £
0·20
+0·71

5 £
0·23
+0·35

6 £
0·55
+0·27

7 £
0·46
+0·24

8 £
0·78
+0·15

9 £
0·53
+0·29

10 £
0·38
+0·47

11 £
0·65
+0·06

12 £
0·49
+0·39

13 £
0·24½
+0·60

14 £
0·03½
+0·12½

15 £
0·36
+0·42½

16 £
0·54½
0·16½

17 £
0·03
0·21
+0·12

18 £
0·15
0·30
+0·13

19 £
0·24
0·13
+0·50

20 £
0·36
0·22
+0·31

21 £
0·14
0·35
+0·13

22 £
0·26
0·40
+0·15

23 £
0·32
0·29
+0·07

24 £
0·57
0·08
+0·26

MONEY ADDITION

Now try these

1 £
0·14
0·25
+0·01

2 £
0·11
0·24
+0·37

3 £
0·46
0·05
+0·30

4 £
0·18
0·32
+0·43

5 £
0·17
0·60
+0·09

6 £
0·29
0·14
+0·55

7 £
0·49
0·28
+0·16

8 £
0·20
0·17
+0·33

9 £
0·16
0·39
+0·25

10 £
0·38
0·19
+0·11

11 £
0·66
0·24
+0·07

12 £
0·45
0·30
+0·20

13 £
$0·04\frac{1}{2}$
0·34
+0·10

14 £
0·50
$0·05\frac{1}{2}$
+0·21

15 £
$0·32\frac{1}{2}$
$0·04\frac{1}{2}$
+0·50

16 £
$0·15\frac{1}{2}$
$0·41\frac{1}{2}$
$+0·22\frac{1}{2}$

17 £
$0·62\frac{1}{2}$
0·14
$+0·03\frac{1}{2}$

18 £
$0·30\frac{1}{2}$
$0·19\frac{1}{2}$
$+0·24\frac{1}{2}$

19 £
$0·41\frac{1}{2}$
$0·07\frac{1}{2}$
+0·26

20 £
$0·28\frac{1}{2}$
$0·49\frac{1}{2}$
$+0·15\frac{1}{2}$

21 £
$0·51\frac{1}{2}$
0·28
$+0·10\frac{1}{2}$

22 £
$0·68\frac{1}{2}$
$0·16\frac{1}{2}$
$+0·05\frac{1}{2}$

23 £
0·02
$0·44\frac{1}{2}$
+0·29

24 £
0·38
0·49
$+0·07\frac{1}{2}$

MONEY SUBTRACTION

First try these

1 £ 0·18 − 0·05	**2** £ 0·15 − 0·03	**3** £ 0·26 − 0·06	**4** £ 0·38 − 0·14
5 £ 0·47 − 0·07	**6** £ 0·43 − 0·21	**7** £ 0·66 − 0·42	**8** £ 0·50 − 0·10
9 £ 0·97 − 0·14	**10** £ 0·84 − 0·53	**11** £ 0·65 − 0·40	**12** £ 0·79 − 0·56
13 £ 0·53½ − 0·32	**14** £ 0·45½ − 0·20½	**15** £ 0·34 − 0·12½	**16** £ 0·27 − 0·06½
17 £ 0·32 − 0·19	**18** £ 0·40 − 0·28	**19** £ 0·35 − 0·05	**20** £ 0·61 − 0·47
21 £ 0·76½ − 0·55	**22** £ 0·82 − 0·51½	**23** £ 0·46½ − 0·38½	**24** £ 0·53 − 0·46½
25 £ 0·97 − 0·79	**26** £ 0·74 − 0·09½	**27** £ 0·95½ − 0·80	**28** £ 0·68 − 0·28½

MONEY SUBTRACTION

Now try these

1 £
0·49
− 0·09
_____

2 £
0·37
− 0·21
_____

3 £
0·80
− 0·60
_____

4 £
0·65
− 0·30
_____

5 £
0·21
− 0·18
_____

6 £
0·53
− 0·49
_____

7 £
0·50
− 0·27
_____

8 £
0·93
− 0·16
_____

9 £
0·65
− 0·38
_____

10 £
0·72
− 0·15
_____

11 £
0·80
− 0·26
_____

12 £
0·54
− 0·09
_____

13 £
0·57
− 0·50
_____

14 £
0·46½
− 0·37
_____

15 £
0·66½
− 0·50½
_____

16 £
0·82
− 0·41½
_____

17 £
0·54½
− 0·25
_____

18 £
0·67
− 0·46½
_____

19 £
0·81½
− 0·36½
_____

20 £
0·78
− 0·58½
_____

21 £
0·89½
− 0·37½
_____

22 £
0·58
− 0·29½
_____

23 £
0·62½
− 0·06½
_____

24 £
0·90½
− 0·51
_____

25 £
0·99½
− 0·69
_____

26 £
0·70
− 0·59½
_____

27 £
0·45
− 0·25½
_____

28 £
0·62½
− 0·14½
_____

MONEY PROBLEMS

First try these

Set 1

1 Mother spent £0·38 on soap and £0·41 on jam. What did she spend altogether?
2 Jack bought one gift at £0·40 and another at £0·45. How much did he spend altogether?
3 Add £0·27 to £0·08½.
4 Find the sum of £0·16 and £0·24½.
5 We paid £0·36 for tea and £0·41 for butter. What was the total cost of these groceries?
6 One bag of nuts cost £0·45 and another cost £0·43. What did the two bags together cost?
7 Yesterday Mother spent £0·46 on biscuits, and today she spent £0·35 on sweets. What did these two things cost her?
8 To £0·40½ add £0·53½.
9 To one-half of £0·68 add £0·48½.

Set 2

1 If you have £0·26 and spend £0·19, how much money have you left?
2 Mary has £0·83 and Susan has £0·65. How much more money has Mary than Susan?
3 Father spends £0·82 each week on papers. How much change does he get if he pays the bill with £0·90?
4 A man gives a shopkeeper £0·50 for an article which costs £0·44. How much change does he get?
5 Add £0·20 and £0·36, and take your answer from £0·95.
6 How much cheaper is a toy that costs £0·49½ than one which costs £0·75?
7 From £0·50½ take £0·28½.
8 I had £0·37 yesterday, but I have £0·64 today. How much have I gained?

MONEY PROBLEMS

Now try these

Set 1

1 Mary bought a toy for £0·68 and had £0·02 change given to her. How much money did she hand to the shopkeeper?
2 Bob had £0·24 and George had £0·15 more than Bob. How much money had they between them?
3 Jones paid me £0·17½, Smith £0·28 and Brown £0·53½. How much money did I get altogether?
4 I took £0·45 to pay a bill, but found I needed £0·37 more. What was the total amount I had to pay?
5 Find the sum of £0·26, £0·08½ and £0·61.
6 To one-quarter of £0·80 add a half of £0·25.
7 In my purse I have £0·05½, £0·10, £0·20 and £0·50. How much money have I to spend?
8 Add £0·31, £0·06 and £0·40.

Set 2

1 A man paid £0·72 for an article instead of £0·81. How much more money should he have paid?
2 From half of £0·98 take £0·23½.
3 I owe the grocer £0·36 and the baker £0·21. If I pay them with £0·50 and £0·20, what change shall I get?
4 From £0·90 take £0·47½.
5 Add £0·59 and £0·15. Subtract £0·28 from your answer.
6 How much less than £0·65 is £0·32½?
7 It costs £0·83 to go to the town by rail and £0·68 by bus. How much cheaper is it by bus?
8 Take £0·29 from the sum of £0·20 and £0·66½.
9 Two boys and three girls earned £0·90 between them. If the boys earned £0·42, how much did the girls earn?

GENERAL REVISION

First try these

Add

1	504	**2**	138	**3**	p	**4**	£
	73		695		20½		0·33
	+125		+47		14		0·57
					+25		+0·01½

Subtract

5	318	**6**	572	**7**	p	**8**	£
	-209		-165		73		0·60
					-36		-0·19½

Multiply

9	17	**10**	21	**11**	35	**12**	47
	×4		×12		×5		×10

Divide

13 5)47 **14** 11)102 **15** 9)136 **16** 6)298

17 Write in figures two thousand, seven hundred and five.

18 At a concert there were 185 men, 306 women and 179 children. How many people were there altogether?

19 At assembly 75 girls and 65 boys were arranged in 7 equal rows. How many children were there in each row?

20 Share 625 counters equally among 5 pupils.

21 A lady bought a doll's dress for 99p but did not like it, and sold it to her friend for 80p. How much money did she lose?

22 A man bought two articles, one costing £0·24½ and the other £0·20. How much change did he get from £0·50?

23 Write down all the even numbers between 39 and 47, and find their sum.

24 From 82½p take 44p.

GENERAL REVISION

Now try these

Add

1	429	2	£	3	p	4	£
	307		0·19		14½		0·71
	+566		0·12½		37		0·03½
			+0·58		+46½		+0·10

Subtract

5	253	6	900	7	£	8	p
	-179		-586		0·93		62
					-0·34½		-27

Multiply

9	28	10	49	11	126	12	274
	×12		×5		×10		×9

Divide

13 7)55   **14** 12)387   **15** 9)875   **16** 5)729

17 Add together £0·06, £0·32 and £0·55.

18 We paid 72p for two small toys. If one cost 48p what did the other cost?

19 A grocer had 8 bags, with 75 kilograms of flour in each bag. How many kilograms of flour altogether?

20 How many times does 9 divide into 3478, and what is the remainder?

21 What number is forty-nine less than two thousand and eight?

22 Find the sum of twelve elevens and one-half of sixty-four.

23 A shopkeeper bought an article for £0·48 and sold it for £0·59½. What was his gain?

24 Share 609 pennies equally among 7 children. How many pennies would each get?

MONEY MULTIPLICATION

First try these

1	p 4 ×2	2	p 3 ×3	3	p 5 ×2	4	p 9 ×2
5	p $8\frac{1}{2}$ ×2	6	p 4 ×5	7	p $6\frac{1}{2}$ ×3	8	p $5\frac{1}{2}$ ×3
9	p 3 ×6	10	p 4 ×9	11	p 8 ×3	12	p $6\frac{1}{2}$ ×4
13	p 10 ×2	14	p $5\frac{1}{2}$ ×6	15	p 11 ×3	16	p 9 ×7
17	p $9\frac{1}{2}$ ×4	18	p $4\frac{1}{2}$ ×7	19	p 10 ×5	20	p 12 ×3
21	p 15 ×5	22	p $11\frac{1}{2}$ ×6	23	p 20 ×3	24	p 24 ×2
25	p 30 ×3	26	p $20\frac{1}{2}$ ×3	27	p 16 ×4	28	p $17\frac{1}{2}$ ×5

MONEY MULTIPLICATION

Now try these

1	p 3 ×4	2	p 10 ×7	3	p 9 ×6	4	p 6 ×7

5	p 4 ×12	6	p 5 ×11	7	p 12 ×5	8	p 14 ×4

9	p $5\frac{1}{2}$ ×8	10	p $7\frac{1}{2}$ ×10	11	p 11 ×9	12	p 20 ×4

13	p $9\frac{1}{2}$ ×8	14	p $6\frac{1}{2}$ ×9	15	p $7\frac{1}{2}$ ×11	16	p $10\frac{1}{2}$ ×7

17	p 6 ×12	18	p $8\frac{1}{2}$ ×10	19	p $9\frac{1}{2}$ ×9	20	p $11\frac{1}{2}$ ×8

21	p 15 ×6	22	p $18\frac{1}{2}$ ×5	23	p $22\frac{1}{2}$ ×3	24	p 24 ×4

25	p $19\frac{1}{2}$ ×5	26	p $28\frac{1}{2}$ ×3	27	p $16\frac{1}{2}$ ×6	28	p 13 ×7

MONEY DIVISION

First try these

1 p
2)8

2 p
2)10

3 p
3)6

4 p
3)15

5 p
2)24

6 p
2)34

7 p
3)21

8 p
3)30

9 p
3)48

10 p
3)60

11 p
3)54

12 p
4)16

13 p
4)36

14 p
4)56

15 p
4)44

16 p
4)80

17 p
5)10

18 p
5)25

19 p
5)45

20 p
5)70

21 p
2)9

22 p
2)21

23 p
2)43

24 p
2)50

25 p
3)42

26 p
5)55

27 p
4)22

28 p
4)60

29 p
2)85

30 p
3)69

31 p
4)52

32 p
5)35

33 p
4)26

34 p
5)65

35 p
4)66

36 p
4)90

MONEY DIVISION

Now try these

1 p 4)64	**2** p 4)88	**3** p 5)75	**4** p 5)90
5 p 6)36	**6** p 6)54	**7** p 7)77	**8** p 6)96
9 p 7)49	**10** p 6)78	**11** p 8)48	**12** p 7)91
13 p 9)27	**14** p 9)63	**15** p 9)81	**16** p 10)40
17 p 11)55	**18** p 11)88	**19** p 10)70	**20** p 12)48
21 p 12)84	**22** p 11)66	**23** p 12)60	**24** p 4)38
25 p 4)76	**26** p 6)39	**27** p 6)99	**28** p 8)52
29 p 10)85	**30** p 12)42	**31** p 8)80	**32** p 10)65
33 p 12)78	**34** p 8)68	**35** p 6)87	**36** p 10)95

MONEY MULTIPLICATION AND DIVISION

First try these

Set 1

1 £	2 £	3 £	4 £
0·03	0·10	0·11	0·08
×3	×6	×4	×7

5 £	6 £	7 £	8 £
0·07	0·05	0·06	0·11½
×9	×8	×12	×3

9 £	10 £	11 £	12 £
0·24	0·12½	0·13	0·17
×2	×5	×6	×4

13 £	14 £	15 £	16 £
0·15	0·23	0·27	0·16½
×5	×3	×2	×6

Set 2

1 £	2 £	3 £	4 £
2)0·04	2)0·20	2)0·52	3)0·09

5 £	6 £	7 £	8 £
3)0·36	3)0·42	4)0·08	4)0·24

9 £	10 £	11 £	12 £
4)0·52	5)0·10	5)0·45	5)0·85

13 £	14 £	15 £	16 £
2)0·15	3)0·28½	4)0·66	5)0·57½

MONEY MULTIPLICATION AND DIVISION

Now try these

Set 1

1 £
0·14
×7

2 £
0·09½
×7

3 £
0·15
×6

4 £
0·11
×8

5 £
0·07½
×12

6 £
0·08½
×11

7 £
0·05½
×10

8 £
0·18½
×5

9 £
0·29
×3

10 £
0·24½
×4

11 £
0·43
×2

12 £
0·26½
×3

13 £
0·10½
×9

14 £
0·12½
×6

15 £
0·04½
×9

16 £
0·06
×11

Set 2

1 £
7)0·14

2 £
7)0·45½

3 £
8)0·56

4 £
8)0·36

5 £
9)0·27

6 £
9)0·99

7 £
9)0·76½

8 £
10)0·50

9 £
10)0·85

10 £
11)0·77

11 £
11)0·49½

12 £
12)0·12

13 £
12)0·30

14 £
12)0·66

15 £
12)0·48

16 £
11)0·38½

MONEY PROBLEMS

First try these

Set 1

1 Find the cost of eight articles at 7½p each.
2 A boy is paid £0·30 for every hour he works. How much will he earn in a morning if he works for 3 hours?
3 How much do I pay for 3 bags at 30p a bag?
4 Multiply £0·05½ by 5.
5 Mother bought nine boxes each costing 8p. What was the total cost?
6 I bought four articles each costing 23p and paid for them with 95p. How much change did I get?
7 What would a girl pay for 6 metres of ribbon at £0·16½ a metre?
8 Find twice the difference between £0·37½ and £0·55.
9 Find the cost of 3 painting books at 25p each.
10 What is 5 times the sum of 3½p and 10½p?

Set 2

1 Share £0·76 equally among 4 children.
2 Four bus tickets cost £0·92. How much does each ticket cost?
3 Five small toys cost 90p altogether. If they were all the same price, what did each cost?
4 How much is £0·58½ divided by 3?
5 A girl and two boys have 50p between them, the boys each having the same amount. If the girl has 25p, how much money has each boy?
6 A man bought 3 tickets. He gave 80p and had 5p change. What did each ticket cost?
7 Two boys and two girls spent £0·96 at the fair altogether. How much did each spend, if all spent the same amount?
8 Add £0·05 to a quarter of £0·72.

MONEY PROBLEMS

Now try these

Set 1

1 Find the cost of 2 articles at 15p each and 7 at 9p each.
2 What is the difference between 3 times £0·24, and £0·69?
3 Find the cost of six 13p bus tickets.
4 Badges for a football team cost 21p each. How much will it cost to buy badges for four members?
5 Father spends 30p a week on sweets and twice as much on tobacco. What does he spend on the two together, each week?
6 Multiply £0·13 by 7.
7 How much is 8 times the sum of £0·07 and £0·01½?
8 Toys cost 24p each. How much will 4 cost?
9 Find 10 times the difference between 53p and 47½p.

Set 2

1 I bought a dozen eggs for 78p. What did 1 egg cost? What would 13 eggs cost?
2 Share £0·84 equally among 8 girls.
3 A man paid for five tickets with 80p and was given 5p change. How much did each ticket cost?
4 Share 68p between John and David, so that John has 24p more than David. (Give John his 24p first.)
5 Divide £0·85½ by 9.
6 Seven tins cost 94½p. How much is that for 1 tin?
7 A girl earns £0·90 for working 3 hours. How much does she earn in 1 hour?
8 Divide £0·93½ by 11.
9 Share £0·66 equally among 12 children.

GENERAL REVISION

First try these

Add

	1		2		3 £		4 p
	87		100		0·13		08
	52		35		0·29		31
	+6		+93		+0·02½		+24

Subtract

	5		6		7 p		8 £
	195		346		40		0·62
	− 87		− 159		− 12½		− 0·17

Multiply

	9		10		11 p		12 £
	21		57		14½		0·26
	×5		×4		×5		×3

Divide

13 3)76 **14** 5)407 **15** £ 3)0·63 **16** p 7)84

17 If a girl put aside 9p a week for 10 weeks, how much would she save?

18 A newspaper has 6 sheets. How many sheets are there in 2 dozen papers?

19 Divide £0·87 by 3.

20 A shopkeeper put 72 tins in a window, arranging them in 8 equal rows. How many tins were there in each row?

21 Find the sum of £0·35, £0·16 and £0·23.

22 How much must be added to 29p to make 92p?

23 Make 17½p four times bigger.

24 Five similar articles cost 85p. What was the cost of each?

25 To 76 add 105, and then take away 147. What is your answer?

26 Find the cost of eight comics at £0·12 each.

GENERAL REVISION

Now try these

Add

1	295	2	472	3	£	4	p
	468		635		0·61		25
	+301		+181		0·28		44
					+0·10½		+16

Subtract

5	361	6	823	7	p	8	£
	-175		-96		78		0·53
					-48½		-0·17

Multiply

9	187	10	264	11	£	12	£
	×11		×8		0·39		0·13½
					×2		×6

Divide

13 10)196 **14** 7)428 **15** p 12)54 **16** £ 8)0·64

17 Divide £0·49½ by 11.

18 The postage on a certain package is 23p. Find the cost of posting 4 packages of this weight.

19 Take a half of forty-eight from a quarter of one hundred and twelve.

20 After paying £0·12, £0·11 and £0·18, how much change would I get from £0·50? And what would the change be from £1·00?

21 Multiply 14p by 7, and take 40p from your answer.

22 Divide 2103 by 12.

23 Add £0·04 to £0·03½, and multiply your answer by 10.

24 Subtract 29p from 96½p, and divide your answer by 9.

MONEY ADDITION

First try these

1 £
  1·00
+3·00
———

2 £
  2·04
+0·30
———

3 £
  3·12
+1·45
———

4 £
  4·61
+2·08
———

5 £
  5·36
+1·02
———

6 £
  4·53
+0·40
———

7 £
  6·11
+2·76
———

8 £
  0·42
+5·17
———

9 £
  3·60
+2·50
———

10 £
  1·41
+5·83
———

11 £
  8·52
+0·84
———

12 £
  4·65
+3·40
———

13 £
  6·95
+1·04
———

14 £
  5·83
+0·21
———

15 £
  7·54
+2·38
———

16 £
  3·46
+2·15
———

17 £
  0·38
+1·46
———

18 £
  5·47
+3·28
———

19 £
  1·65
+2·15
———

20 £
  4·29
+0·36
———

21 £
  2·38
+6·74
———

22 £
  3·54
+5·69
———

23 £
  0·87
+4·05
———

24 £
  6·26
+0·77
———

25 £
  0·59
+0·41
———

26 £
  7·68
+5·73
———

27 £
  4·06
+3·94
———

28 £
  6·29
+3·85
———

MONEY ADDITION

Now try these

| 1 | £
3·70
+4·19 | 2 | £
8·05
+2·63 | 3 | £
6·24
+3·52 | 4 | £
1·31
+7·75 |

| 5 | £
12·94
+0·60 | 6 | £
4·56
+11·82 | 7 | £
10·73
+9·51 | 8 | £
15·28
+13·47 |

| 9 | £
23·58
+14·25 | 10 | £
18·67
+26·94 | 11 | £
30·85
+0·15 | 12 | £
14·96
+56·93 |

| 13 | £
68·09
+12·72 | 14 | £
52·13
+19·87 | 15 | £
40·51
+60·24 | 16 | £
29·41
+83·65 |

| 17 | £
70·00
+43·07 | 18 | £
68·45
+30·19 | 19 | £
22·82
+97·65 | 20 | £
100·69
+29·58 |

| 21 | £
4·36½
+7·51 | 22 | £
12·04½
+10·60½ | 23 | £
29·35
+8·13½ | 24 | £
45·20½
+17·99½ |

| 25 | £
94·85
+10·07½ | 26 | £
26·23½
+34·76½ | 27 | £
40·38½
+57·83 | 28 | £
8·74½
+90·69½ |

MONEY SUBTRACTION

First try these

1 £ 3·76 − 2·41	**2** £ 4·17 − 3·07	**3** £ 6·98 − 4·26	**4** £ 5·86 − 3·83
5 £ 12·65 − 9·12	**6** £ 10·59 − 6·43	**7** £ 8·92 − 4·01	**8** £ 13·19 − 8·06
9 £ 6·27 − 4·51	**10** £ 9·18 − 3·60	**11** £ 8·63 − 1·93	**12** £ 11·45 − 6·82
13 £ 13·07 − 2·95	**14** £ 12·36 − 7·43	**15** £ 14·85 − 9·65	**16** £ 10·24 − 9·81
17 £ 9·46 − 5·07	**18** £ 11·51 − 6·19	**19** £ 13·80 − 10·16	**20** £ 12·75 − 3·68
21 £ 9·32 − 2·47	**22** £ 14·00 − 9·13	**23** £ 10·48 − 3·19	**24** £ 12·56 − 8·72
25 £ 15·08 − 1·99	**26** £ 13·63 − 7·85	**27** £ 10·50 − 9·63	**28** £ 17·21 − 8·52

MONEY SUBTRACTION

Now try these

1 £
   4·39
 − 2·05
 ─────

2 £
   8·64
 − 3·43
 ─────

3 £
   17·85
 − 10·40
 ─────

4 £
   12·96
 − 8·06
 ─────

5 £
   7·49
 − 2·63
 ─────

6 £
   18·56
 − 3·91
 ─────

7 £
   9·42
 − 8·72
 ─────

8 £
   10·17
 − 4·65
 ─────

9 £
   28·41
 − 16·27
 ─────

10 £
    36·50
 − 12·35
 ─────

11 £
    42·73
 − 10·69
 ─────

12 £
    50·24
 − 19·18
 ─────

13 £
    47·36
 − 15·48
 ─────

14 £
    98·04
 − 7·27
 ─────

15 £
    76·58
 − 40·99
 ─────

16 £
    94·00
 − 35·63
 ─────

17 £
    51·41
 − 35·01
 ─────

18 £
    70·80
 − 2·87
 ─────

19 £
    95·23
 − 68·45
 ─────

20 £
    86·84
 − 71·39
 ─────

21 £
    $38·24\frac{1}{2}$
 − 26·72
 ─────

22 £
    $40·58\frac{1}{2}$
 − $11·39\frac{1}{2}$
 ─────

23 £
    57·20
 − $41·83\frac{1}{2}$
 ─────

24 £
    49·02
 − $38·96\frac{1}{2}$
 ─────

25 £
    $75·19\frac{1}{2}$
 − 16·23
 ─────

26 £
    64·83
 − $20·31\frac{1}{2}$
 ─────

27 £
    89·36
 − $82·75\frac{1}{2}$
 ─────

28 £
    92·07
 − $51·27\frac{1}{2}$
 ─────

MONEY MULTIPLICATION

First try these

1 £
1·23
×2
_____

2 £
2·40
×2
_____

3 £
3·01
×2
_____

4 £
1·54
×2
_____

5 £
2·11
×3
_____

6 £
4·32
×3
_____

7 £
1·01
×4
_____

8 £
0·22
×4
_____

9 £
5·18
×2
_____

10 £
3·29
×2
_____

11 £
6·17
×3
_____

12 £
4·06
×3
_____

13 £
3·24
×4
_____

14 £
7·13
×4
_____

15 £
2·51
×2
_____

16 £
3·72
×2
_____

17 £
4·60
×3
_____

18 £
1·81
×4
_____

19 £
6·50
×5
_____

20 £
2·65
×2
_____

21 £
5·76
×2
_____

22 £
9·07
×3
_____

23 £
4·95
×3
_____

24 £
10·24
×4
_____

25 £
8·53
×4
_____

26 £
11·25
×5
_____

27 £
7·08
×5
_____

28 £
0·24
×5
_____

MONEY MULTIPLICATION

Now try these

1 £
   2·31
   ×6
   _____

2 £
   3·04
   ×6
   _____

3 £
   1·65
   ×7
   _____

4 £
   2·43
   ×7
   _____

5 £
   5·92
   ×8
   _____

6 £
   10·01
   ×8
   _____

7 £
   8·47
   ×9
   _____

8 £
   11·30
   ×9
   _____

9 £
   3·14
   ×10
   _____

10 £
   5·08
   ×10
   _____

11 £
   4·20
   ×11
   _____

12 £
   9·74
   ×11
   _____

13 £
   8·36
   ×12
   _____

14 £
   0·97
   ×12
   _____

15 £
   10·12
   ×8
   _____

16 £
   4·28
   ×11
   _____

17 £
   5·09
   ×12
   _____

18 £
   6·43
   ×8
   _____

19 £
   12·70
   ×7
   _____

20 £
   3·57
   ×9
   _____

21 £
   4·23½
   ×4
   _____

22 £
   7·06½
   ×5
   _____

23 £
   11·59
   ×8
   _____

24 £
   6·35
   ×11
   _____

25 £
   5·07½
   ×8
   _____

26 £
   3·84
   ×12
   _____

27 £
   9·53½
   ×7
   _____

28 £
   20·12½
   ×8
   _____

MONEY DIVISION

First try these

1 £
2)4·80

2 £
2)6·28

3 £
3)9·60

4 £
3)6·39

5 £
3)12·99

6 £
4)16·80

7 £
4)12·48

8 £
4)8·84

9 £
5)10·50

10 £
5)25·55

11 £
2)3·40

12 £
2)8·76

13 £
2)9·34

14 £
2)8·08

15 £
3)9·42

16 £
3)10·71

17 £
3)12·09

18 £
4)16·16

19 £
4)17·60

20 £
4)21·36

21 £
5)35·50

22 £
5)21·00

23 £
5)28·45

24 £
6)24·60

25 £
6)30·06

26 £
6)22·80

27 £
6)43·74

28 £
2)67·54

29 £
2)0·30

30 £
3)85·47

31 £
4)0·92

32 £
4)2·96

33 £
5)87·25

34 £
5)0·95

35 £
6)69·48

36 £
6)0·78

MONEY DIVISION

Now try these

1   £   2   £   3   £   4   £
7)21·70   7)29·40   7)35·21   7)19·81

5   £   6   £   7   £   8   £
8)16·80   8)41·60   8)28·56   8)56·08

9   £   10   £   11   £   12   £
7)3·29   8)5·04   9)27·90   9)38·70

13   £   14   £   15   £   16   £
9)49·86   9)7·29   10)30·10   10)57·20

17   £   18   £   19   £   20   £
10)4·70   11)88·11   11)70·40   11)64·79

21   £   22   £   23   £   24   £
12)36·12   12)63·60   12)54·72   12)10·80

25   £   26   £   27   £   28   £
7)83·23   8)0·48   10)97·90   10)4·60

29   £   30   £   31   £   32   £
12)0·12   11)96·03   9)0·36   7)2·24

33   £   34   £   35   £   36   £
9)76·59   9)0·54   11)1·10   12)81·24

MONEY PROBLEMS

First try these

Set 1

1 Find the cost of 2 lorry loads of sand at £42·75 a load.
2 Last week Mother paid the grocer £7·12, the baker £3·63 and the milkman £2·95. What did she pay the three altogether?
3 A watch and clock together cost £56·75. If the watch cost £18·50, what did the clock cost?
4 Five dresses, each costing the same amount, were bought for £92·50. What was the price of 1 dress?
5 Share £3·54 equally among 3 children.
6 A cowboy suit costs £19·80. Find the cost of 4 cowboy suits.
7 Father bought three shirts at £11·99 each. What was the total cost?
8 Find the difference in value between 50p and £5·00.

Set 2

1 How much must a boy save each month, for 6 months, to buy a model yacht costing £21·60?
2 Find the total sum of money paid for a camera costing £19·20, a rugby ball costing £10·50 and a football costing £8·90.
3 Find the cost of 5 fountain pens at £5·80 each.
4 Find the sum of £6·43, £22·07½ and £17·10.
5 A school had £80 left to spend on library books, but bought books costing only £72·15. How much money was still to be spent?
6 For three months our coal cost us £37·36, gas £22·94 and electricity £20·02. What sum did we pay altogether for light and heat?
7 Three similar toys cost £8·37 altogether. What did each cost?

MONEY PROBLEMS

Now try these

Set 1

1 Three dresses cost £75·00. What was the cost of each dress?
2 A man spent £12·50 on a shirt, £64·80 on a suit and £4·70 on a tie. How much did he spend altogether?
3 Find the cost of four pairs of shoes at £20·90 a pair.
4 For 2 weeks Father paid £87·30 in rent for our holiday caravan. How much is that a week?
5 We saved £66·03 for our summer holiday. At the end of the holiday we still had £3·84 left over. How much had we spent?
6 Divide £58·32 equally among 9 children.
7 We need £87·67 more for a television set and aerial. At the moment we have £59·81. How much does the television set and aerial cost?

Set 2

1 Find the cost of a gross of eggs at £0·69 a dozen.
2 Find the cost of taking a football team (11 boys) and a master to another school, if the return fare is £0·84 for the master, and the boys travel at half price.
3 Tom has £1·53, Bob has £0·47 more than Tom, while George has £0·30 more than Bob. How much money have they altogether?
4 What must be added to £15·71 to make £32·59?
5 Seven similar articles were bought at the market for £96·95. What was the cost of 1 article?
6 Share £102 equally among 3 boys and 3 girls.
7 A man had £80·00. He owed his butcher £17·48, his milkman £20·19 and his baker £5·82. How much money had he left after paying his bills?

GENERAL REVISION

First try these

Add

1		2	£	3	£
	59		1·12½		15·26
	7		2·34		9·87
+18		+0·07		+1·59	

Subtract

4	619	5	£	6	£
	−387		16·18		11·40
			−2·75		−0·93½

Multiply

7	98	8	£	9	£
	×4		1·16½		0·38½
			×3		×6

Divide

10 6)138   **11** £ 8)10·08   **12** £ 5)6·55

13 A piece of rope 92 metres long is cut into lengths of 4 metres. How many pieces can be cut?

14 Find the total cost of four books, if each cost £7·95.

15 Six similar scarves cost £23·40. How much for 1 scarf?

16 What number multiplied by itself makes 81?

17 I pay a grocery bill of £3·90½ with £4·00. How much change shall I get?

18 Find the sum of 1 dozen, 1 score and 1 gross.

19 Subtract six hundred and twenty-seven from eight hundred.

20 Find the total cost of a table priced £29·90 and a desk priced £45·20.

21 Multiply £0·82½ by 10.

22 Share £5·07½ among 5 children, so that each gets the same amount.

GENERAL REVISION

Now try these

Add

1	396	2	£	3	£

1   396
     487
 +125

2   £
 20·68½
  0·93½
+13·21

3   £
 15·70
 40·25½
 +2·04

Subtract

4   482
 −376

5   £
 40·61
−19·52

6   £
101·37½
 −2·60

Multiply

7   396
  ×6

8 £
5·91
 ×7

9 £
2·68
 ×9

Divide

10 12)3870

11   £
10)93·3

12   £
11)100·10

13 One train set cost £84·14 and another cost £76·80. How much cheaper was the second one?

14 What number multiplied by itself makes 6 less than 150?

15 What is the cost of a dozen dresses at £19·60 each?

16 Divide 1476 by 8.

17 Share £32·78 equally among 6 boys and 5 girls.

18 Find the sum of 4 gross and 10 score.

19 Multiply the difference between £1·53 and £0·64 by 7.

20 Find the total cost of 9 Christmas cakes at £6·20 each, and a dozen buns at 14p each.

21 A cyclist travelled 84 metres in 12 seconds. If he travelled at a steady speed, how many metres did he cover in 1 second?

22 Write in figures three thousand, three hundred and twenty.

SETS

All can try these

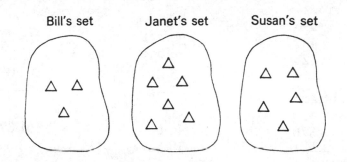

Bill's set   Janet's set   Susan's set

Bill has a set of triangles, so has Janet and so has Susan.

1 Whose set has fewest triangles?
2 How could you find out who had fewest triangles without counting them?
3 If Bill and Janet put their triangles together how many triangles would there be in the new set?
4 What number must be put in the box?
   $3 + \square = 9$
5 How many triangles would you have to add to Susan's set so that it has as many triangles in it as Janet's set has?
6 What number must be put in the box?
   $6 - \square = 1$
7 If all three children put their triangles together how many triangles would be in the new set?
8 If the triangles in the new set formed in question 7 were divided to make two equal sets, each having the same number of triangles, how many triangles would there be in each set?
9 If Janet and Susan put their triangles together how many more triangles would be in this new set than in Bill's set?

MORE ABOUT SETS

All can try these

1

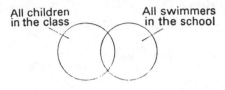

One set contains all the children in the class. The other set contains all the swimmers in the school, some of whom are in this class. Which children will be found where the sets intersect (or overlap)?

2

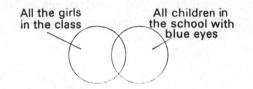

One set contains all the girls in the class. The other set contains all children in the school with blue eyes. Some girls with blue eyes are in this class. Which children will be found where the sets intersect?

3

Set *A* contains all large coloured squares. Set *B* contains red squares which vary in size. If the sets intersect what shapes shall we find in the intersection?

4 Look at the diagram in question 3. Set *A* contains all men and women with dark hair. Set *B* contains all women. What kind of persons shall we find in the intersection of the sets?

SETS AND ADDITION

All can try these

1

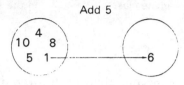

By adding 5 to each member of the first set we can get members of a new set of numbers. Copy the diagram, mark in the numbers in this second set, and draw an arrow from each member of the first set to the corresponding member of the second set. An example, using number 1 in the first set, is done for you.

2

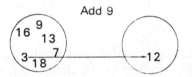

Copy this diagram. Write in the numbers of the second set, and draw the arrows from the members of the first set to the corresponding members of the second. One number in the second set is placed for you.

3

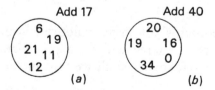

In both examples copy the diagrams and complete them. Write in the numbers of the second set and draw arrows from the members in the first set to the corresponding members of the second.

SETS AND SUBTRACTIONS

All can try these

On the last page we transformed the members of one set into the members of another set by adding. Now we transform the members of the first set by subtraction.

1

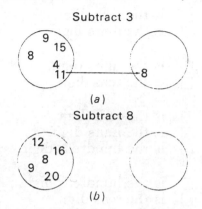

Subtract 3

(a)

Subtract 8

(b)

In both (a) and (b) copy the diagrams. Mark in the numbers of the second set, and draw arrows from the members of the first set to the corresponding members of the second set. An example is done for you.

2

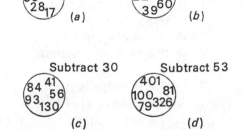

Subtract 15 (a)

Subtract 21 (b)

Subtract 30 (c)

Subtract 53 (d)

In the four examples copy the diagrams and complete them. Mark in the numbers in the second sets, and draw arrows from the members of the first sets to the corresponding numbers in the second sets.

DIGITS

All can try these

What number has to be placed in each of the boxes below?

1 In 35,   ☐   is the tens digit.
                ☐   is the units digit.

2 In 79,   ☐   is the units digit.
                ☐   is the tens digit.

3 In 140,   ☐   is the tens digit.
                ☐   is the units digit.
                ☐   is the hundreds digit.

4 In 258,   ☐   is the hundreds digit.
                ☐   is the tens digit.
                ☐   is the units digit.

5 In 1562,   ☐   is the thousands digit.
                ☐   is the units digit.
                ☐   is the hundreds digit.
                ☐   is the tens digit.

6 In 2009,   ☐   is the hundreds digit.
                ☐   is the tens digit.
                ☐   is the units digit.
                ☐   is the thousands digit.

7 In 3010,   ☐   is the hundreds digit.
                ☐   is the thousands digit.
                ☐   is the units digit.
                ☐   is the tens digit.

8 Make the largest possible number and the smallest possible number from the figures 3, 1, 4, 0.

SHAPES

All can try these

1 Look at this shape which is known
as a square.
  (a) How many sides has it?
  (b) What do we know about the
      lengths of the sides of a square?
  (c) How many angles has a square?

  (d) What name do we give to the angles of a square?

2 Look at this shape which is
known as a rectangle.
  (a) How many sides has it?
  (b) What do we know about the lengths of the sides
      of a rectangle?
  (c) How many angles has a rectangle?
  (d) What name do we give to the angles of a rectangle?

3 Here is a drawing of a rectangular block like a match
box.
  (a) How many faces has it?
  (b) How many edges has it?
  (c) How many face angles
      has it?
  (d) What do we know about
      the size of its face angles?
  (e) How many more faces
      are there just like the top, *EGBA*?

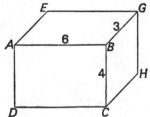

  (f) How many more faces are there just like the end
      face *BGHC*?
  (g) If *CD* is 6 cm long, how long is *EG*?
  (h) If *AE* is 3 cm long, how long is *CH*?
  (i) If *GH* is 4 cm long, how long is *AD*?
  (j) Complete this sentence: '*AC* is a ———— of the
      face *ABCD*'.

TRUE OR FALSE

All can try these

When we write $2 + 4 = 6$, the $=$ sign means 'represents the same number as', so 6 stands for the same number as the sum of 2 and 4. Thus the sentence $2 + 4 = 6$ is **true**.

The sign $>$ means 'is greater than'. Thus $8 > 5$ is also a **true** sentence, but $9 > 16$ is **false**.

We also use the sign $<$. This stands for 'is less than'. Thus $12 - 3 < 10$ is **true** but $5 < 3$ is **false**.

1 Are these sentences **true** or **false**?

(a)	$9 + 7 = 16$
(b)	$2 + 13 < 12$
(c)	$4 + 5 > 10 - 1$
(d)	$14 + 2 = 20 - 4$
(e)	$11 + 9 = 7 + 2 + 6$
(f)	$5 - 2 + 8 < 12$
(g)	$6 + 9 > 7 + 5 + 4$
(h)	$13 + 5 = 9 + 8$
(i)	$5 \times 2 > 3 \times 3$
(j)	$28 \div 2 < 11$
(k)	$32 \div 4 = 24 \div 3$
(l)	$19 + 13 + 4 > 50 - 14$

2 What numbers must be placed in the boxes to make these true sentences?

(a)	$5 + 3 = \square + 4$
(b)	$11 + \square = 1 + 10$
(c)	$4 + \square + 6 = 2 + 18 - 7$
(d)	$17 + 5 = 30 - \square$
(e)	$12 \times 3 = \square \times 6$
(f)	$8 \times 6 = 4 \times \square$
(g)	$36 \div 6 = \square \div 2$
(h)	$50 \div 2 = \square \times 5$
(i)	$45 \div 9 = \square \times 1$

TRUE SENTENCES

All can try these

1 Write down one of the symbols $=$, $>$, $<$ to make each of the following into a true sentence:

(a)	$4 + 7$	12
(b)	$10 - 3$	6
(c)	$12 - 8$	3
(d)	$20 + 5 + 0$	17
(e)	18	$29 - 10$
(f)	$14 + 8 + 9$	$20 + 11$
(g)	5×6	9×3
(h)	$4 \times 4 \times 4$	8×8
(i)	$20 \div 10$	3
(j)	$40 + 8 - 6$	7×6
(k)	$49 - 1$	12×4
(l)	37	7×5
(m)	$25 + 36 + 1$	$80 - 4 + 1$
(n)	$100 - 41$	$59 + 0$
(o)	$121 - 20$	100
(p)	$193 + 8$	2×100
(q)	$162 - 60$	110
(r)	$500 - 199$	300
(s)	$200 + 98 + 1$	$400 - 99$
(t)	$5 \times 3 \times 4$	$120 \div 2$

2 Make the following into true sentences putting the smallest possible whole number in the box:

(a) $\quad 4 \times \square > 19$

(b) $\quad \square \times 9 > 41$

(c) $\quad 7 \times \square > 36$

3 Make the following into true sentences putting the largest possible whole number in the box:

(a) $\quad \square \times 3 < 10$

(b) $\quad 6 \times \square < 70$

(c) $\quad 13 \times \square < 40$

LENGTH AND WEIGHT

First try these

Addition

1	m	**2**	m	**3**	m	**4**	m
	6		13		10		19
	+9		+7		+12		+15

5	cm	**6**	cm	**7**	cm	**8**	cm
	8		18		21		$23\frac{1}{2}$
	+11		$+3\frac{1}{2}$		+16		$+4\frac{1}{2}$

9	kg	**10**	kg	**11**	kg	**12**	kg
	4		$15\frac{1}{2}$		$10\frac{1}{2}$		14
	+11		+3		$+20\frac{1}{2}$		+19

13	g	**14**	g	**15**	g	**16**	g
	5		23		6		24
	+17		+12		+32		+30

Subtraction

1	m	**2**	m	**3**	m	**4**	cm
	9		16		28		30
	-5		-7		-14		-20

5	cm	**6**	cm	**7**	kg	**8**	kg
	$14\frac{1}{2}$		32		$26\frac{1}{2}$		34
	-8		$-16\frac{1}{2}$		-25		$-13\frac{1}{2}$

9	kg	**10**	g	**11**	g	**12**	g
	40		25		32		41
	$-9\frac{1}{2}$		-19		-12		-17

LENGTH AND WEIGHT

Now try these

Addition

1	m	2	m	3	m	4	cm
	20		38		$14\frac{1}{2}$		$17\frac{1}{2}$
	+16		+23		$+15\frac{1}{2}$		+33

5	cm	6	cm	7	kg	8	kg
	52		65		27		42
	$+29\frac{1}{2}$		+18		$+30\frac{1}{2}$		+57

9	kg	10	g	11	g	12	g
	$18\frac{1}{2}$		50		49		34
	$+74\frac{1}{2}$		+36		+49		+25

Subtraction

1	m	2	m	3	m	4	m
	32		$48\frac{1}{2}$		61		$52\frac{1}{2}$
	–14		–39		$–25\frac{1}{2}$		$–36\frac{1}{2}$

5	cm	6	cm	7	cm	8	cm
	70		37		$82\frac{1}{2}$		65
	–21		–18		–56		$–20\frac{1}{2}$

9	kg	10	kg	11	kg	12	kg
	$95\frac{1}{2}$		40		69		86
	$–78\frac{1}{2}$		$–9\frac{1}{2}$		–50		$–27\frac{1}{2}$

13	g	14	g	15	g	16	g
	53		76		94		66
	–24		–65		–25		–48

LENGTH AND WEIGHT PROBLEMS

First try these

Set 1

1 We could measure the length of a garden in metres. Write down two other examples in which we could measure the distance in metres.

2 We could measure the width of a book in centimetres. Write down two other examples in which we could measure the distance in centimetres.

3 How many centimetres are equivalent in length to (*a*) 1 m, (*b*) 1½ m?

4 A rod is half a metre long. How many cm is that?

5 Add 13 cm, 8 cm and 2½ cm.

6 One line is 24 cm long and the other is 15½ cm. What is the difference in length between the lines?

7 From point A to point B is 80 m and from point B to point C is 93½ m. How far is it from A to C through B?

8 While Jack ran 200 m, Bill ran 72 m. Who ran faster, and how much further did the winner run?

Set 2

1 We could measure the weight of a basket of apples in kilograms. Write down two other examples in which we could measure the weight in kilograms.

2 We could measure the weight of a letter in grams. Write down two other examples in which we could measure the weight in grams.

3 How many grams weigh the same as (*a*) 1 kg, (*b*) ½ kg?

4 Add 2000 g to 7½ kg. Give your answer in kg.

5 One box weighed 80 kg and another weighed 43 kg. What was the difference in weights of the boxes?

6 The weights of four baskets of pears were 15, 12, 18 and 20 kg. What was the total weight of pears?

7 A letter weighed 13 g. What was the total weight of 12 similar letters?

8 How much more is one half of 50 g than a half of 32 g?

LENGTH AND WEIGHT PROBLEMS

Now try these

Set 1

1 Draw straight lines (using chalk and a piece of rope) on the playground and measure their lengths to the nearest whole metre.

2 Draw some straight lines in your exercise book and measure their lengths to the nearest whole centimetre.

3 Jack's height is 115 cm and Susan's is 102½ cm. How much taller is Jack?

4 Bill walked 1250 m, then 960 m. Altogether he had to walk 2750 m. How much further had he to go?

5 If each piece of wood is 4½ m long, what length of wood is there in 9 such pieces?

6 A coil of rope is 100 m in length. How many pieces, each 12 m long, can I cut from it? What length of rope will be left over?

7 A field is in the shape of a rectangle. It is 120 m long and 80 m wide. How far is it all round the field?

Set 2

1 One child weighed 38 kg and another weighed 29½ kg. What was (a) the total weight of the two children, and (b) the difference in their weights?

2 One gram costs 3p. How much will 25 g cost?

3 One balance pan holds weights of 27 g, 14½ g and 6 g. The other pan holds weights of 1½ g, 25 g and 21 g. Will the pans be in balance?

4 How many grams weigh the same as 12 kg?

5 One metre of a fine wire weighs 5 g. What will 200 m of the wire weigh? Give your answer in kg.

6 Twelve boxes, each of the same weight, weigh 1152 kg. What does each box weigh?

7 A postman can carry 15 kg of letters on his rounds. How many letters, each weighing 10 g, can he carry as he sets out from the Post Office?

GENERAL REVISION

All can try these

1	2	3	4
268	801	317	137
312	− 257	× 9	× 12
+ 653			

5	6	7	8
p	£	8)2087	£
12½	2·37½		5)79·85
× 6	× 11		

9 From the sum of £4·02 and £10·69½, subtract £5·38.

10 The side of a square table is 1 metre. What is the distance all round its edge in centimetres?

11 What number must be placed in each of the boxes to make the following true sentences:
(a) $18 \div 9 = 22 \div \Box$
(b) $16 + 20 - 3 = 11 \times \Box$

12 Find the cost of 10 dozen eggs at £0·72 per dozen.

13 How many faces has a brick? What is the shape of each face?

14

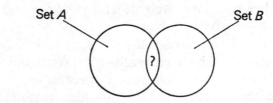

Set A contains all the males in a town. Set B contains all those persons in that town who own a bicycle. Which persons are included in the intersection of the sets (marked by ?)?